MW00609258

THE PROFIT MACHINE
IN THE HOSPITAL BASEMENT

THE PROFIT MACHINE

IN THE HOSPITAL BASEMENT

Turning Your Lab Into
An Economic Engine

KATHLEEN A. MURPHY, PHD

ELLSWORTH PRESS
ANN ARBOR, MICHIGAN

Printed in the United States of America by Ellsworth Press.

ISBN 978-0-9973320-0-1 (hardback) — ISBN 978-0-9973320-1-8 (softbound) — ISBN 978-0-9973320-2-5 (ebook)

Library of Congress Control Number: 2016936234

CONTENTS

Introduction iii

Chapter 1
History of the Laboratory Industry 1

Chapter 2
Why is Outreach so Misunderstood? 11

Chapter 3
The Rationale for Outreach 23

Chapter 4
The Battle for Market Share between Hospitals
and Independent Laboratories. 33

Chapter 5
Strategy 55

Chapter 6
Operational Infrastructure. 65

Chapter 7
Financial Considerations. 77

Chapter 8
Structural Requirements. 97

Chapter 9
Sales. 107

Chapter 10
Risk versus Reward 123

Acknowledgements 139

Notes 141

References 145

Index 147

About the Author 153

INTRODUCTION

My passion is empowering laboratories to become economic engines for hospitals and health systems. After all, I have spent more than three decades in the health care field. In all that time, I have never before witnessed a rate of change and disruption anywhere close to what we are now experiencing.

Sure, we all lived through diagnosis-related groups, managed care, and now accountable care, but where does it end? How can we continue to offset declines in reimbursement?

Most hospitals and health systems today are understandably focused on cost reductions. While controlling costs is certainly a major part of the equation, lowering cost alone is not sufficient. Haven't we all heard that you can't shrink yourself to greatness? There has to be a revenue component. Yet, hospitals have given up revenue for dead. The operating assumption is that there are no new sources of revenue and, if there is one, it is suspect, low margin, non-core, too complicated, too hard, etc.

I want to open your eyes to the real money left on the table in your laboratory—*money that you cannot afford to overlook in the current environment.*

Every hospital and health system has sunk costs in laboratories that are required for serving inpatients and outpatients. They have a substantial investment in facilities, information technology, laboratory equipment, automation, and staff, but use only 20 to 30 percent of capacity on a 24/7 basis. The excess capacity can be leveraged to bring in more work from the community, with work typically done on off-shifts when hospital volume is low.

By providing a competitive offering, laboratory outreach programs can compete and win against large national and regional laboratories (such as Quest Diagnostics and LabCorp). Outreach brings material new revenues and margins to hospitals looking for ways to offset decreasing reimbursement from traditional service lines. The secret is in the structure, funding, and execution as a serious business entity.

Over 90 percent of hospitals perform some outreach work, but the vast majority of outreach programs are small businesses that are underfunded and run as side-line businesses. Because of this, outreach has a bad rap. It is viewed by many hospital executives as a business that is too difficult, not part of the core business, or not sufficiently profitable to pursue. However, there are dozens of successful laboratories that have generated over $100 million in revenue with 30 percent operating margins.

What is different about these programs? They are treated as a separate P&L, funded based on performance, and allowed autonomy to compete in the external market. They operate outside of the typical hospital bureaucracy as serious business entities. This book elucidates the differences between the successful businesses and the majority of "mom-and-pop" operations. It gives you a step-by-step approach to leveraging the powerful hospital profit machine that is laboratory.

Progressive hospital executives who adopt this approach will see benefits accrue from financial, operational, service, and quality perspectives. Who, today, is in a position to overlook the following?

- Material new revenue and operating margin
- Improved unit cost and efficiencies
- Better services for all patient types, inpatient and outpatient included
- Superior quality for managing population health

You simply cannot afford to lose out on this opportunity. It is your fiduciary responsibility to put all preconceived notions aside and learn the secrets from a lab insider. You will never look at your laboratory in the same way again. Let's shed a light on the incredible profit potential hiding in your hospital basement.

CHAPTER 1

HISTORY OF THE LABORATORY INDUSTRY

An understanding of laboratory as a profit machine requires some knowledge of the history of the industry. Many of our preconceived notions—good and bad—come from historical events. We will start with a brief overview of the history of the industry to provide a proper context and foundation for prevailing views.

1950s: THE EARLY YEARS

The first independent laboratories started off with aggressive discounting out of the gate. Kings County Research Laboratories of Brooklyn, New York, offered unlimited clinical laboratory testing to doctors for $75 per month. Noting Kings County's early success, United Medical Laboratories (UML) of Portland, Oregon, copied the model with some restrictions, requiring a minimum volume to secure the highest discounts. UML began as a vitamin supplement distributor. In order to provide proof of efficacy for its supplements, UML started offering basic laboratory testing. Growth was rapid in the early years, and the owners discovered that the medical laboratory business was more attractive financially. They then focused on growing this component of the business and maintained a separate, small company for vitamin supplements.

1950–1959
Early Labs: *King's County Research Laboratories*, Brooklyn, NY; *United Medical Laboratories*, Portland, OR
- Offered unlimited testing for fixed fee
- Exploration into discounted fees

1960s: EXPERIMENTATION

New entrants into the laboratory industry during the 1960s were either pathologist-owned laboratories or pharmaceutical companies that either purchased a laboratory or started their own businesses:

- Dr. Paul Brown, a pathologist, started MetPath in New York, New York.
- An attempt by Upjohn, a pharmaceutical company, to enter the industry by purchasing UML was foiled. Instead, Upjohn started its own company, called Laboratory Procedures, initially based in Woodland Hills, California, and eventually in King of Prussia, Pennsylvania.
- Another pharmaceutical company, SmithKline Beecham, entered the laboratory market by acquiring Biskind Laboratory in San Francisco, California, from a pathologist.

Early laboratories experienced rapid organic growth. For example, UML's business grew to $20 million during this decade, processing 10,000 patient requisitions per day.

1960–1969

New Entrants: *MetPath*, New York, NY; *Upjohn (Laboratory Procedures)*, Woodland Hills, CA; *SmithKline*, San Francisco, CA

- First profiles for screening
- Discounted fees
- Physician markups
- Anti-markup laws
- Federal regulation of laboratories (CLIA)
- Removal of restrictions for interstate licensing
- First automated instrument
- Independent lab acquisitions begin

The 1960s was a decade of experimentation. The first screening profiles were developed. Laboratories targeted physicians by heavily promoting the advantages of discounted fees and physician markups as a way to drive new margins for their practices. A few states passed anti-markup laws in response. Two new regulatory developments occurred: restrictions on interstate licensing for laboratories were removed, further promoting growth; and because of the proliferation of laboratories and concerns about quality, the Clinical Laboratory Improvement Act (CLIA) was passed in 1967. A key development driving the growth of the industry was the automation of chemistry instruments available to large laboratories.

1970s: EXPANSION

Six new entrants came into the market in the 1970s:

1. W. R. Grace, a chemical company, which owned several laboratories in Ohio and in Saginaw, Michigan.
2. Bristol–Myers (another pharmaceutical company) developed a laboratory subsidiary in Southern California that was poorly run and eventually sold to MetPath at fire sale pricing.
3. Bioran, a new startup in Cambridge, Massachusetts, developed a very successful business, ultimately being acquired 20 years later for $180 million.
4. Damon Clinical Laboratories acquired several laboratories throughout the U.S.
5. Revlon, a cosmetics company, entered the industry by acquiring a laboratory in Detroit, Michigan.
6. ICN Pharmaceuticals acquired UML in 1972 after a computer replacement crippled company operations. MetPath then acquired this laboratory in 1978 after ICN mismanaged it.

This was the decade of rapid expansion of independent laboratories, both from organic growth and acquisitions. Some states passed direct billing or anti-markup laws to circumvent physician profits from marking up the cost of laboratory work, but this did little to hamper growth. These laws were passed in California, New York, Michigan, and New Jersey, to name a few states. A new organization, the American Clinical Laboratory Association (ACLA), formed to lobby for the growing independent laboratory industry.

1970–1979

New Entrants: *ICN Pharmaceuticals*; *Bristol Myers (Biomedical Procedures)*, CA; *Bioran*, Cambridge, MA; *Damon Clinical Laboratories*; *W. R. Grace*, Cincinnati, OH; *Revlon*

· Direct billing laws
· Independent lab acquisitions continue
· First fledgling hospital-based outreach programs
· First independent lab-hospital management contracts
· American Clinical Laboratory Association formed

There were two firsts in this decade: the first fledgling hospital-based outreach programs emerged, often encouraged by pathologists with percent of gross compensation arrangements, and the first management contracts between a hospital and an independent laboratory were executed in 1972 by MetPath in Council Bluffs (Jenny Edmunson Hospital) and Ottumwa (St. Joseph Hospital), Iowa. These developments are significant in that they represent a new level of competition between hospitals and independent laboratories—each entering the other's market to compete.

1980s: COMPETITION

Regulations favoring hospital pricing nurtured the steady development of hospital-based outreach programs. A survey by Root Associates (1987) identified laboratory outreach as a popular strategy, with 61 percent of hospitals having implemented an outreach program. These programs were small by today's standards, with an average revenue of about $1 million (compared to an average and median today of $19 million and $12 million, respectively). Even though individual programs were small, collectively this hospital competition was taking a sizable chunk of market share away from independent laboratories.

1980–1989
- Regulations favor hospital pricing
- Big shift of hospital labs into outreach
- Independent labs focus on physician partnerships
- First hospital-independent lab joint venture
- Shift towards moving hospital labs offsite
- Independent lab acquisitions continue
- Corning acquires MetPath

In response, some laboratories, particularly Mayo Clinic (as the Medical Laboratory Network) in California, Meris Lab in California, and MetPath in New York, created physician partnership laboratories. The goal was to align with physicians as a growth strategy, with physicians having a 50 percent ownership stake.

The second strategy was to align with hospitals in the first formal joint ventures. *Modern Healthcare* highlighted this approach in a 1984 article about a deal with Damon Clinical Laboratories and MacNeal Memorial Hospital in Berwyn, Illinois (just outside Chicago).[1] Damon managed the laboratories and drove $1 million in cost savings for the hospital. In return, Damon was able to use the new laboratory to grow the outreach business.

Pathologists jumped into the fray of outreach when the Tax Equity and Fiscal Responsibility Act (TEFRA) of 1982 threatened pathology reimbursement. A 1984 *National Intelligence Report* article highlighted a new strategy by pathologists to form joint ventures with one or more hospitals.[2] Laboratories were moved offsite to form regional laboratory networks to drive down costs and grow volume.

This was a decade of increased competition. Hospital-based outreach, physician partnerships, and pathologist joint ventures put more pressure on large independent laboratories, making acquisition an increasingly important part of their growth strategy.

Also during this time, MetPath grew exponentially until it reached revenues in excess of $110 million when it was sold to Corning in 1982.

1990s: GREED AND EXCESS

The '90s brought a black eye to the laboratory industry. In response to reductions in Medicare reimbursement, independent laboratories developed bigger and bigger panels, added unnecessary high reimbursement tests, performed duplicate billing, instituted reflex testing, and charged for mere calculations—all to drive reimbursement. When it was over, government investigations dubbed "Labscam" won settlements totaling $874 million. Two laboratory executives served time in prison. As a result, all the major laboratories were forced to sign "corporate integrity agreements" to do business with the government.

In a 180-degree reflex action in response to inappropriate practices and an effort to control costs, Medicare instituted diagnosis-related groups (DRGs) as a fixed reimbursement for hospital stays. Private insurers instituted managed care and capitation. Some independent laboratories accepted totally untenable capitation rates as low as $0.50 per member per month to secure exclusive agreements. Within the span of one decade, the independent laboratory industry went from excess to deprivation.

In this environment, Corning Clinical Laboratories grew to $2 billion before spinning off the business as Quest Diagnostics.

1990–1999
- Managed care
- Reductions in fee schedule
- Capitation
- DRGs
- Bigger and bigger panels
- Reflex testing
- Labscam—$874 million in fines
- Lab executives imprisoned
- Corporate integrity agreements
- Hospital lab consolidation
- Beginning of regionalization—hospital lab networks

On the hospital front, two new trends emerged: consolidation of hospital laboratories across a system (and occasionally between disparate systems) to lower costs; and the beginnings of regionalization—forming hospital laboratory networks to develop negotiating leverage with major insurance companies. The most famous laboratory network was Joint Venture Hospital Laboratories (JVHL) in Michigan. Coming together as a network of 80 hospitals in southeast Michigan, JVHL was able to capture exclusive contracts from independent laboratories and essentially drive independent laboratory competitors out of the market.

2000s: AGGRESSIVE M&A FORMS A DUOPOLY
In the 2000s, aggressive merger and acquisition (M&A) activity by two major independent laboratory companies set the stage for what would later be viewed as a duopoly of two mega-laboratory companies. Quest Diagnostics (Quest) grew to $7.5 billion. Laboratory Corporation of America (LabCorp), a merger of National Health Laboratories and Roche Biomedical Laboratories grew to $1.7 billion.

In parallel, consolidation and regionalization trends for hospital laboratories continued. More hospital laboratories entered the outreach market. In fact, outreach became a mainstream strategy, with over 70 percent of hospitals reporting an active program.

2000-2009
· Aggressive M&A by independent labs
· Roll-up strategy produces duopoly
· Regionalization and consolidation of hospital labs

2010s: DISRUPTION

The last decade has been highly disruptive. Acquisitions by large independent laboratories have continued. After 30 years of raging acquisitions, few small independent laboratory targets remain. Quest and LabCorp have begun to purchase outreach business from hospitals that need cash or no longer view outreach as consistent with hospital strategy. The vast majority (over 80 percent) of hospitals are now running outreach programs. Those in excess of $50 million to $100 million have become acquisition targets, although both LabCorp and Quest have purchased smaller businesses opportunistically.

2010-PRESENT
· More aggressive M&A by independent labs
· Independent labs buy hospital outreach programs
· Independent labs expand outside of industry
· Health care companies buy labs
· Outside companies buy into lab industry
· Ramping up of regionalization and consolidation of hospital labs
· Affordable Care Act
· Reductions in reimbursement and bundled payments
· Pay for quality and outcomes

New entrants to the market include non-laboratory health care companies, private equity companies, other health care companies, and even insurance companies. Some are getting into the market and others are opting out, each seeing something that the others do not and looking for synergies to their existing business.

As of 2015, Quest's growth was stagnant at $7.5 billion and LabCorp had grown to $6 billion. In 2015, LabCorp purchased Covance, a $2.5 billion contract research organization providing drug development and animal testing services with an extensive laboratory infrastructure. This made LabCorp an $8.5 billion behemoth, surpassing Quest revenue for the first time. And the duopoly is revealed—each of these companies is larger than any other by a factor of 10.

CHAPTER SUMMARY

The evolution of the independent laboratory industry started with research laboratories or vitamin suppliers that used laboratory testing as a supplement to their main businesses. The laboratory business was an afterthought, a sideline. After realizing the financial potential, these early entities morphed into clinical laboratory companies and started the growth of what was to eventually become an $83 billion industry.

· Early entrants were wholesalers to physicians who, in turn, marked up pricing to supplement practice income.

· Early development of profiles and automation fueled growth.

· Eliminating restrictions on interstate business allowed for strong regional and national growth.

· All types of companies entered the laboratory market: chemical, cosmetics, pharmaceutical, glass manufacturers, private equity, and pathologist-owned/operated.

· In the early to middle years, growth was mostly organic. Later on, rapid expansion was fueled by aggressive M&A.

· The large independent laboratories (Quest and LabCorp) tried various strategies to capture market share: physician partnerships, joint ventures, and management agreements for hospital laboratories.

· The greed and excess of the 1990s cast a shadow over the industry, ultimately resulting in $874 million in fines, imprisonment of executives, and corporate integrity agreements. The reflexive response by government and private insurers involved dramatic reimbursement cuts, managed care, and capitated payments.

· In the last 20 years, a duopoly has been established through aggressive acquisition by Quest and LabCorp. They are each now $7.5 billion to $8.5 billion companies that have tapped out the private laboratory market and are turning to hospital-based outreach programs to fuel growth.

In the next chapter, we will put all this into context. Quest and LabCorp have become laboratory behemoths in their own right in the independent laboratory market, yet they represent a small portion of the market overall—somewhere between 10 and 12 percent each. Where is the rest of the business? You guessed it—at the hospitals! The next chapter provides an overview of: the laboratory market in terms of current value; how it is distributed among independent for-profit laboratories, hospitals, and physician office laboratories; the different market segments by laboratory specialty; and the do's and don'ts of competitive positioning.

CHAPTER 2

WHY IS OUTREACH SO MISUNDERSTOOD?

Many people have a negative reaction to the idea of outreach, defined as the business of hospital laboratories "reaching" out or marketing their laboratory services to the market at large to bring in additional volume, revenue and margin. Why? Consider the story of a colleague of mine prior to elective surgery.

Jim's doctor referred him to the hospital's patient service center, located in the basement of the medical office building, to have his blood drawn for pre-operative laboratory work. He impatiently waited his turn for 30 minutes or more and, once interviewed, was told that the laboratory did not accept his insurance. He asked why the doctor would send him there if it couldn't process his laboratory work. In turned out, his doctor's office never bothered to check with the laboratory.

The poor fellow was instructed to go to another laboratory five miles away. He asked what the cost would be if he simply paid for the laboratory work himself. After all, he was a busy man—he had other commitments and did not have time to drive all over town simply to get his blood drawn. The laboratory technician said she had no idea how much the testing would cost, but that he would receive a bill on his credit card. Sure, sir, would you just sign this blank check before I draw your blood? Jim left shaking his head and went home unhappy, to say the least.

On a subsequent day, he went to another laboratory after verifying by phone that it accepted his insurance. He relayed his story about the hospital patient service center and that technician told him that he was lucky he came to her laboratory since the cost of the blood test at this laboratory was $60. He would have been charged $200 at the local hospital. So poor service and higher prices too? What a deal!

Some would say that this example is not an accurate description of the service provided by the average hospital-based outreach program. I agree. Usually it is much worse!

For starters, outreach is totally different from traditional hospital business. Inpatients and outpatients have no choice but to use the hospital laboratory. This assumption that the business is "captive" generates all manner of poor service.

Let's start with patient access. Outpatient specimen collection sites are often located far from parking lots and in remote areas of the hospital. Patients need the latest GPS device to navigate the labyrinths of the facility. If they are lucky enough to find the collection site, they have to go through a lengthy registration process that is largely unnecessary for laboratory work and treats patients needing a quick blood draw the same as those undergoing complex surgery. It is painful and they haven't even had their blood drawn yet!

Once through registration, patients languish in yet another queue, reminiscent of the registry of motor vehicles, to have their blood drawn. There are no standards for wait time, nor is the site staffed according to volume by hour of day. Patients wait up to an hour or more to be served. They are unhappy with the service, but no one seems to notice or care. After all, this is the standard process for all patients.

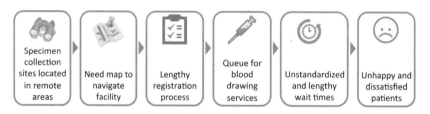

FIGURE 2.1: THE STANDARD HOSPITAL LABORATORY PROCESS

Contrast this experience with a visit to a patient service center owned by an independent regional or national laboratory. The services are designed around patient needs. Patient service centers are strategically located in office buildings near the high volume physician clients. Parking is abundant. They have extended hours so that patients can come after work and on Saturday mornings. The patient service center is on the first floor, close to the building entrance. Patients are greeted and logged in, so that wait time can be measured and managed within the 15-minute advertised customer guarantee. The more progressive outfits have scheduled appointments to assuage longer wait times at certain predictable, high-volume times of day (early morning and lunch hour). Staff members perform a "quick registration" and make a photocopy of the patient's insurance card only if necessitated by recent changes. The patient's blood is drawn, and they are out and on their way in 15 minutes on average. Management staffs the site according to volume by hour of day, measures and tracks patient wait times, and makes adjustments regularly to ensure meeting the customer guarantee. This is what a patient service center (with the emphasis on *service*) should be.

> ▶ Outreach has a unique nomenclature. Patients are referred to as "nonpatients," because they are neither hospital inpatients nor outpatients. Non-service to nonpatients is the unfortunate outcome in non-outreach-oriented hospitals.

How does that compare to your laboratory? If you had a choice— and many times patients do—where would you go? It is no longer safe to assume that patients are captive and must go to *your* laboratory. You can't treat them like prisoners! Patients make choices with their feet and complain to their doctor if forced to go to a laboratory that is non-service-oriented. Word spreads. Each unhappy client tells seven other people and they then repeat the story, which gets more and more distorted and outrageous with each telling. Just like the games we played as kids where you whispered something into someone's ear, when it makes the rounds of all your friends, the story is totally different. You can't afford to mess with your reputation in that manner.

Outreach has a unique nomenclature to distinguish it from traditional hospital business. These patients are referred to as "nonpatients," because they are neither hospital inpatients nor outpatients. No one ever set out to intentionally deliver non-service to nonpatients, but that is the unfortunate outcome in non-outreach-oriented hospitals.

Another way outreach differs from other hospital services is that it is complicated. The laboratory must have a new, extensive, competitive offering that is different from outpatients to be viable in the external market. Outreach requires a new infrastructure (sales, patient service centers, logistics, information technology platforms for doctors to order tests and receive results, client services, and billing/collections). It is a complicated chain of services which must be provided seamlessly and flawlessly. Each laboratory is only as good as the weakest link in the chain, as shown in Figure 2.2.

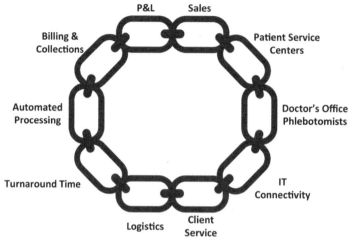

Your lab is only as good as the weakest link in the chain.

FIGURE 2.2: CHAIN LINKING OF OUTREACH SUPPORT

Having all these services does *not* make you stand out in a highly competitive market. It only allows you to play the game. A more detailed description of the infrastructure requirements can be found in Chapter 6. Some argue the point that they do outreach without all the accouterments. This is not something of which to be proud. These laboratories may get some passive, walk-in business from patients that live nearby or are referred by local physicians. A small number of doctors and patients tolerate the poor service for convenience or loyalty. Is this how you want to be known? Businesses like these are inevitably quite small, with less than $1 million in revenue. The reason is obvious: it is a self-limiting model.

What if I told you that your business should actually be two, three, or several times your current size with better service? Would you still be proud?

Just when you've started to forget about the poor service and you think it can't get worse, the bill arrives. It is a startling two to five times the cost of the same testing at a national laboratory. And now that you have a higher deductible and copayment, you are responsible for any amount over the "low ball" rate charged by the national laboratory to get an exclusive contract. The bad news: you are out of pocket for up to hundreds of dollars. That's right. You get poor service *and* get charged more!

In addition to being different and complicated, the third factor contributing to misunderstandings about outreach is that the value is not understood or appreciated. The problem is structural. Because outreach is an entrepreneurial business trapped within a nonprofit, there is a lack of transparency about the financial performance of outreach. According to the *Thirteenth Comprehensive National Laboratory Outreach Survey* conducted by Chi Solutions, Inc. (Chi) in 2014, only 42 percent of outreach programs have a formal profit and loss (P&L) statement produced by hospital finance. Of those that do, the majority estimate net revenue because reimbursements for hospital patients and outreach are co-mingled.[1] Unless the laboratory has a separate provider number or outsources billing, it is impossible to track clean, collected (net) revenue. What true business doesn't know how much money is collected? One that doesn't stay in business for very long.

Furthermore, there is no standard methodology for allocation of costs. Some organizations insist on allocating hospital and laboratory overhead to outreach. This is an unnecessary drag on profitability. Only costs that can be attributable to outreach are those that would be eliminated if you exited the business. Would hospital overhead costs go away? Would you still have the same hospital executive team? How about laboratory overhead? Would the administrative and medical directors go away if the hospital exited the outreach business? What about the overhead required to run the hospital side of the business? The obvious answer is no. What about patient service centers, sales representatives, courier costs, specialized information technology software, and variable supply and labor expenses for performing testing? Absolutely!

A recent engagement provides a good example of how misallocation of expenses can make outreach look unprofitable. We were called in to assess strategic options for a hospital-based outreach business that appeared to have very low profitability: an operating income of about $500,000 (2.3 percent) on a $21.4 million business. This laboratory was set up as a separate company and operated as an independent laboratory. Margins for an independent laboratory are a little lower (about 20 percent) than a hospital laboratory that operates under the hospital identification number and fee structure (about 30 percent). This laboratory was way off the mark at 2.3 percent. The client wanted to know if it should continue to invest in the business, or monetize it and use the cash for other hospital priorities. Our analysis is shown in Table 2.1.

TABLE 2.1: HOSPITAL OUTREACH CURRENT STATE

in 000's	Hospital	Outreach	Total
Revenue:			
Inpatient	$9,317		9,317
Outreach		32,371	32,371
Total Gross Charges	9,317	32,371	41,688
Contractual Adjustments		(20,021)	(20,021)
Bad Debt		(396)	(396)
Net Patient Revenue	9,317	11,953	21,271
Other Operating Revenue	99	54	153
Total Operating Revenue	9,417	12,007	21,424
Expenses:			
Salary and Benefits	5,510	4,057	9,568
Professional Fees and Purchased Services	2,289	2,064	4,353
Internal Assessment	396	491	887
Medical Supplies	2,327	1,752	4,079
Depreciation and Amortization	61	76	137
Other	640	1,266	1,906
Total Expenses	11,223	9,707	20,930
Operating Income	$(1,806)	$2,300	$494
Operating Income %	-19.2%	19.2%	2.3%
Key Statistics			
Test Volume	671	903	1,574
Net Revenue per Test	$14.03	$13.30	$13.61
Total Cost per Test	$16.72	$10.75	$13.30
Salary and Benefit Cost per Test	$8.21	$4.49	$6.08
Supply Cost per Test	$3.47	$1.94	$2.59

The margin calculation run by the client included the cost of all hospital-based services and outreach rolled into one P&L. This is appropriate from an accounting perspective, since the laboratory company provided services for the hospital and for the outside business, but most of the costs are associated with running the hospital laboratory. These costs include facilities, laboratory equipment, information technology, automation, labor, and supplies. If the client were to exit the outreach business, it could reduce its costs by about 20 percent. Getting out of the business would eliminate the cost of the outreach infrastructure (patient service centers, phlebotomists, couriers, sales, supply cost, and some technologists), but the laboratory would still not shrink to profitability. The cost of maintaining a laboratory to support the hospital on a 24/7 basis would remain.

However, segregating hospital and outreach costs showed a much different story. The outreach P&L had an operating margin of 19.2 percent when allocations for hospital laboratory overhead were removed. The hospital services had an operating margin of -19.2 percent while outreach was +19.2 percent—total opposites yet the startling differences in performance were not discernable when the two businesses were intermingled (2.3 percent).

This example demonstrates the importance of proper cost allocation. This outreach business was actually operating only slightly below the typical operating margin for independent laboratories (19.2 percent versus 20 percent). Fortunately, this story had a happy ending. Understanding the true profitability of outreach led this organization to invest in growing this business. It had held off on making critical investments in information technology. Growth had slowed as a result, topping out at $12 million. Now, senior executives are committed to make the investment to fuel the next stage of growth.

Following this construct for allocation of costs, the average hospital-based outreach program has an operating margin of about 30 percent. Put into context with the overall hospital performance, 30 percent looks pretty good against the average hospital net income of 3.1 percent! Yes, we are talking a ten-fold difference in margins, based on the latest information for average hospital profits.[2] There's no doubt that outreach would be seen in a different light with full transparency regarding the performance of this business. It would be a game-changer. Instead of being viewed as a high volume, low margin business, outreach would be viewed as a significant margin generator for the hospital. I will build on this topic further in Chapter 6.

You know that old saying "if we believe we can, we can, and if we believe we can't, then we can't"? In the same way, our beliefs about outreach are a self-fulfilling prophecy. If we believe that outreach is good business and we develop the business model accordingly, then it is successful. And if we believe it is not profitable and non-core, and we half-heartedly piece together a fragmented, non-competitive offering, then it will not succeed... just like we thought. This circular, self-fulfilling reasoning is shown below in Figure 2.3. We get what we believe—it is a self-fulfilling prophecy.

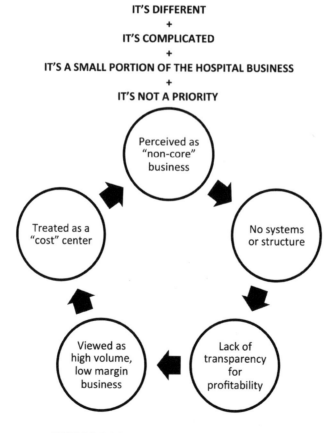

FIGURE 2.3: THE SELF-FULFILLING PROPHECY OF OUTREACH

So how does this happen? Some may take offense at this statement: my experience is that most nonprofit hospitals do *not* function like businesses. Historical payment models have not pressured hospitals sufficiently to make them run like true businesses. They take years to come to decisions that would be made in a fraction of the time in the for-profit world. Politics can still hijack good business decisions. Often the tough, appropriate choices are only made as a last resort or when there is a crisis. This is part of the frustration of being a for-profit business in a nonprofit world. Granted, this is beginning to change with new performance-based reimbursement models. We are only at the beginning of the evolutionary curve. Financial performance will get much worse before things change for the better.

Here is an example. Chi performed strategic options assessments for two different hospital systems that had growth potential. One had been approached by an acquirer to sell its $42 million laboratory business on the West Coast and wanted to know if it should sell or continue to grow the business. The other was interested in a growth plan, but revenue had plateaued for the last two to three years. Each wanted to know the answers to three questions:

- Can we grow the business and, if so, by how much?
- Should we scale the business back to clients of strategic value including physicians and skilled nursing facilities that are affiliated with the hospitals?
- Should we exit, monetize the business, and use the funds to support other nonprofit services?

Both organizations had opportunity for growth, but had to adjust pricing down from the hospital outpatient fee schedule to be able to capture more market share. This was a difficult decision. We argued that it was low risk; they felt the opposite. One client worried that insurers would downgrade outpatient reimbursement to the lower price offered in the market at large. With 30 years in the business, we have never heard of that happening. All the client could see was a potential loss of $8 million in outpatient revenue. The second client had a similar loss in the first year of a five-year pro forma if it reduced pricing to be more competitive. Interestingly, this client was willing to take a reduction in the first year because the plan forecasted a growth of more than four times over the next 10 years.

I checked back with both clients one year after the completion of Chi's study. I wanted to write a case study about the commonality of issues, but include different views on how to solve them. Would you believe that neither organization had taken any action after a whole year and they still have not done so nearly two years later? In a for-profit world, these executives would have "left their organizations to pursue other opportunities." In business, not making a decision is much worse than making the wrong decision. It is a career-limiting event. In one case, there was a lack of alignment among the management team. The other client was accustomed to growing revenue through a self-limiting strategy of charging exorbitantly high prices to outpatients and didn't see the need to look for alternate sources of revenue. No urgency, no decision.

Here's an example of poor, irrational management of outreach. Let's say that I have made a case for outreach as a profitable business for hospitals. I will provide more detail later, but for the sake of discussion, let's assume that a well-run outreach program contributes margin to the hospital. If revenue was down elsewhere in the hospital, would you include the laboratory in an across-the-board budget cut? Would you "kill the goose that laid the golden egg?" I have seen this happen on many occasions. I have also seen growth constrained by lack of adequate capital and resources. At best, arcane business practices such as these marginalize outreach programs. At worst, they increase losses for the hospital as a whole. The rational approach would be to cut budgets for services that are not profitable and reapportion funds to further grow good business lines like laboratory. Rarely have I seen this happen. We have to ask ourselves why.

One reason is that the skills and experience to run a successful multimillion dollar, for-profit business are different from those required to run a service organization for hospital inpatients and outpatients. Chi's *Thirteenth Comprehensive National Outreach Survey* found that the average and median revenues of outreach programs are $12 million and $9 million, respectively. In the business world, companies of this size would have an experienced CEO and management team and all the trappings of a going concern. In the hospital world, outreach is run by a mid-level laboratory manager or administrator whose training is typically in medical technology. While many have furthered their education in business, most lack true business experience; they are not experienced business operators accustomed to P&L responsibility. They run the outreach business as a sideline in addition to their hospital job. My company, Chi, is smaller than the average outreach program. How long do you think we would be in business if I ran it as a sideline in a highly competitive business environment? What if I spent the vast majority of my time gardening and traveling, and Chi was a "hobby" business. The results would not be pretty.

From all of the above, you can see that outreach is not for the faint of heart. It's different, it's complicated, it's not transparent. It's a small portion of the hospital business and therefore not a priority. It's a self-fulfilling prophecy. What if on top of all these obstacles, you tried to manage a $12 million business without even the most basic business information? Here are some eye-opening statistics from Chi's *Eleventh Comprehensive National Outreach Survey*:[3]

- Less than 25 percent of respondents have access to hourly and daily metrics for client service, including rate of abandoned calls, hold time for incoming calls, and number of calls per service representative per day.
- Thirty-seven percent cannot track missed courier pickups, and 25 percent don't have any means of knowing if they lost a patient specimen.
- Less than 25 percent know net revenue or profitability by client.
- Sixty-six percent don't know their bad debt rate.
- Over three-quarters do not know their days sales outstanding (DSO).

When asked if they had the information, management reports, and key performance indicators to manage their business, the vast majority of survey participants responded negatively, as shown in Figure 2.4. I like to call this "managing by Braille."

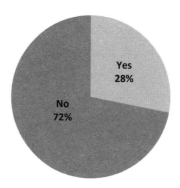

Almost three-quarters of outreach programs report that they do not have the information they need. Is that any way to run a business?

Source: Chi Solutions, 11th Comprehensive National Laboratory Outreach Survey, June 2012.

FIGURE 2.4: ACCESS TO INFORMATION TO MANAGE BUSINESS

CHAPTER SUMMARY

It is the culmination of all the following factors that result in outreach being so misunderstood:

· It's different from other hospital business.
· It's complicated, requiring a whole new infrastructure.
· It lacks transparency and standardization for measuring financial performance.
· It is a small, for-profit business stuck within a large, bureaucratic, nonprofit organization.
· It is a self-fulfilling prophecy.
· It does not have the information to manage the business.

This is merely the tip of the iceberg. We will be discussing each of these factors in more detail throughout the book. Perhaps now you are beginning to get an idea of why outreach can have a bad rap?

CHAPTER 3

THE RATIONALE FOR OUTREACH

The balanced scorecard, popularized by Kaplan and Norton from Harvard Business School,[1] is a good construct to evaluate outreach from four different perspectives: finance, customer, efficiency, and learning and growth.

TABLE 3.1: BALANCED SCORECARD (BSC) FOR LABORATORY

Finance	Customer
■ Economies of scale lead to lower unit cost for inpatients, outpatients, and nonpatients ■ New revenue and margin	■ Better service from local (versus national) laboratory ■ Comparison of results across the patient continuum (hospital, physician office, long-term care, medical home)
Efficiency	**Learning and Growth**
■ Leverage spare capacity and sunk cost in facilities, equipment, and staff ■ Most scalable of all hospital services	■ Partner with physicians and payers on utilization management, reducing the cost of poor quality and managing population health

From a finance viewpoint, outreach provides economies of scale and reduces unit cost for all types of patients: inpatients, outpatients, and nonpatients. For hospital systems with sizable outreach programs, the impact of scale is material. We performed a study for a three-hospital system with a $42 million outreach program that was considering its strategic options. Should they grow the business or exit and monetize the asset for a one-time payout? The system was shocked to learn that the cost of testing for inpatients and outpatients would increase by 50 percent if it exited the outreach business. Was it worth a one-time payout of one to two times revenue when unit costs would go up by 50 percent indefinitely? Not to this system. They were doing well financially and viewed the laboratory as an economic asset to build for the future. It was the proverbial goose that laid the golden egg.

Laboratory is the perfect recurring revenue model allowing for substantial (greater than or equal to 20 percent) growth year over year, roughly doubling every five years. How many other hospital services enjoy that kind of growth record? A minority of cash-strapped hospital systems have exited outreach for a one-time infusion of cash. Ironically, some have re-entered the market when their non-compete clauses expired. This says a lot about the value of outreach, which is, perhaps, seen more clearly retrospectively. Hindsight is always clearer than foresight. This topic will be discussed in greater detail in subsequent chapters.

> ▶ Laboratory drives a disproportionate share of hospital profits: less than five percent of costs can drive greater than 50 percent of EBITDA (earnings before interest, taxes, depreciation, and amortization). Who knew that laboratory could be an economic engine driving such a disproportionate share of profits?

The most compelling story is the impact on hospital revenues and margins at a time when every hospital is scrambling to adapt to lower reimbursements. Would you rather be "shuffling the chairs on the deck of the Titanic" waiting for the dreaded intersection of the cost and revenue curves plaguing most hospitals, as shown in Figure 3.1?

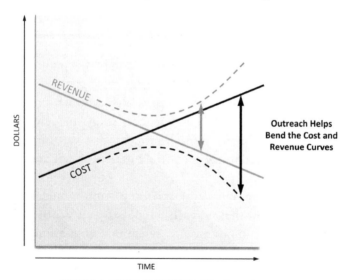

FIGURE 3.1: IMPACT OF OUTREACH FOR HEALTH SYSTEMS

Or would you rather be proactive and find new sources of revenue and margin to mitigate declining reimbursement? This is not a rhetorical question. According to the most recent poll of hospital CEOs by

Healthcare Executive,[2] maintaining financial viability is the number one concern. Yet all the follow-up discussions are about managing cost and mitigating risk; there is absolutely nothing about new sources of revenue. It's as if health care executives have been so beaten down by declining reimbursements for years that the idea of new revenues and growth is simply incomprehensible or considered fools' gold. One hospital executive said that she feels like she is standing in quicksand every single day and it is her goal simply to survive without being consumed by the sand.

Outreach is rational and compelling for those willing to take a little risk. But taking risk in health care is a bit of an oxymoron. Seems we've stumbled on another reason. Health systems are very risk-adverse. Given this context, it is understandable that outreach can be overlooked or considered too good to be true. We have to have our head out of the sand to see the opportunity. We have to be thinking beyond day-to-day survival.

The financial rationale for outreach is strong. Hospital-based outreach programs have operating margins of 30 percent, while health systems as a whole were reported to have an average operating margin of 3.1 percent in 2014.[3] Who's calling the kettle black? Yes, you are reading the numbers correctly. We're talking a tenfold difference in margin for laboratory versus the organization as a whole. What about comparing outreach to the large national or regional laboratories? Here's a surprise: outreach programs perform even better than the national, multibillion dollar, for-profit companies such as Quest Diagnostics and LabCorp, according to Chi's *Thirteenth Comprehensive National Laboratory Outreach Survey*.

TABLE 3.2: OUTREACH PROGRAMS VS. NATIONAL LABORATORIES

	Outreach Program[1]	Quest Diagnostics	LabCorp
Revenue per Requisition[2]	$58.33	$44.34	$44.28
Revenue Growth[2]	5.3%	-4.3%	-1.0%
Profitability[3]	28.0%	18.9%	15.8%

[1]All numbers reported as averages; data from Chi's Comprehensive National Laboratory Outreach Survey, 2014.
[2]Year-over-year increase excluding acquisitions.
[3]Measured as contribution margin or pre-tax profit.

Quest and LabCorp data from Laboratory Economics, February 2014.

As Table 3.2 shows, hospital-based outreach programs outperformed the national laboratories on three key financial metrics: (1) revenue per requisition, (2) organic growth year over year, and (3) profit margin measured as operating margin for hospitals and pre-tax profit for the national laboratories.

Revenue per requisition, a key measure of reimbursement per patient encounter, was 32 percent higher for hospital outreach ($58 for hospital outreach compared to $44 for Quest and LabCorp). This advantage is due in part to a higher reimbursement rate for hospitals compared to independent laboratories. I have long suspected that payers will, at some point in the future, go to a single standardized (that is, lower) fee schedule for all outpatient and nonpatient business. How long this hospital advantage will remain is a topic of discussion in a subsequent chapter. For the foreseeable future, we do not see this changing. Nor are we concerned if it does. Hospitals have significant margin opportunity to compensate for declining reimbursements for some time.

For the next financial metric, growth, the national laboratories were dead in the water for organic growth, with -4.3 percent and -1.0 percent growth rates for Quest and LabCorp, respectively. For years, the national laboratories have been growing through voracious acquisition. They have now purchased all the small- to medium-sized independent laboratories and for the last few years have been focusing on buying hospital outreach programs.

On operating margin, the third key financial metric, hospital-based outreach programs beat the nationals handily (28 percent compared to 19 percent for Quest and 16 percent for LabCorp). Do these results surprise you? You and most industry analysts. The nationals are always trying to convince hospitals, physicians, payers, and other stakeholders that they have superior financial performance. The facts do not bear out their assertion. In fact, quite the opposite is true. The main reason is that hospitals have the power to leverage their sunk costs in laboratory facilities, equipment, staff, and spare capacity and only add variable costs as outreach volume scales. This provides a tremendous economic advantage.

Following the financial quadrant, the impact to the customer is seen in better turnaround-time-to-results at local hospital laboratories. National laboratories deploy a sophisticated salesforce to convince doctors that they provide better service at lower cost. They collect specimens and transport them hundreds of miles to about a dozen regional laboratories across the country. This is accomplished by a sophisticated and costly network of courier vehicles and airplane transport. Hundreds of thousands of specimens are transported out of the local community every day. These regional laboratories are large, highly automated production facilities that crank out the work overnight and transmit routine test results to clients early the following morning. Because of proximity, the local hospital laboratory can actually provide better turnaround-time-to-results—the same day if required. Hospital laboratories can turn around results in the afternoon for specimens collected in the morning. That kind of turnaround time allows physicians to make interventions earlier for patients with abnormal results, enabling better patient care.

The second reason that national laboratories claim they are better than hospital laboratories is cost. They achieve a level of scale rarely replicated by even the largest hospital systems, but at what cost? The nationals may have taken scale to an extreme that no longer serves the purpose. What if the extent of consolidation at the national laboratory level has exceeded the limits of scale, in fact achieving anti-scale? What if the cost of scale is reflected in SG&A, such as the cost of deploying a national salesforce or an extensive logistics network? Do we believe that this highly consolidated business model is cheaper than the local hospital? Really?

It depends on what we are measuring. Because of their scale, the national laboratories undoubtedly beat out the local hospital on production costs (supplies, equipment, and labor to perform testing). They have the luxury of functioning as a third-shift factory operation, while hospitals must provide service 24 hours a day, seven days a week, even during times of low volume, because of patient acuity. Production cost and total costs are not the same. We do not have access to the full cost of testing at the national laboratories. Publically available information cannot be found at this level. My questions are meant to provoke further exploration and understanding of the value proposition.

Although hospital-based laboratories do not approach the scale of the nationals, the impact of additional volume is still profound, perhaps more so than for the nationals as shown in Figure 3.2.

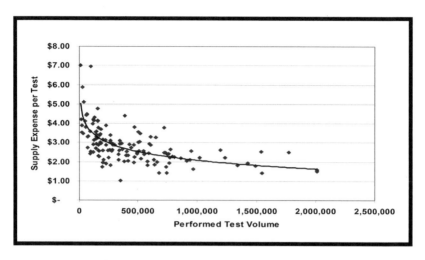

FIGURE 3.2: ECONOMIES OF SCALE FOR SUPPLY EXPENSE

The largest benefit of volume is seen early in the development of a new outreach program. As the graph shows, the biggest impact on unit cost is found in the first 500,000 added tests.

Another framework to examine costs between outreach and national laboratories is to look at variable cost. As mentioned earlier, most hospital laboratory costs (facilities, equipment, and staff) are sunk costs required for providing services to hospital inpatients. The additional cost of outreach testing is really variable rather than fully-loaded cost. Variable costs include supplies, labor, information technology, and the support infrastructure (sales, patient service centers, logistics, client service, etc.) required to compete in the market. Using the variable cost model, hospitals are definitely competitive with the national laboratories.

If there were no national laboratories, could hospital or system laboratories achieve the same economies of scale on a regional basis? Absolutely. In fact, scale has the same impact on efficiency for hospitals. Laboratory is unique in this regard. No other hospital service can scale in a manner comparable to laboratory. Practically speaking, with rare exception, traditional hospital services are limited to a defined market from which patients are willing to travel. Progressive hospitals have been able to scale their laboratory outreach program for hundreds of miles.

They have become regional powerhouses, capturing significant market share away from the national laboratories. They leverage scale to lower unit cost but not to the extreme of national laboratories.

Let's take this one step further and ask if, as a society, we set out to design the ideal process for delivering laboratory services, would we choose to rebuild the redundant infrastructure of the national laboratories separate and distinct from hospitals? Is that the most efficient use of health care dollars? Can we afford that duplication, especially when the benefit accrues to multibillion dollar, for-profit companies? What if, instead, we leveraged the sunk cost in hospital laboratories to provide regional services?

In addition to better service, the other big impact in the customer quadrant is the continuum of care advantage for hospitals. Large commercial laboratories can duplicate services outside of the hospital, but rarely do they serve as operators of hospital laboratories. As a result, the vast majority of the time, testing is fragmented among multiple laboratories. Patients pass through this process first as a hospital inpatient, to a hospital outpatient, to doctors' offices served by national laboratories, to skilled nursing and/or rehabilitation facilities and/or medical homes served by yet another laboratory. (The national laboratories do not service nursing homes due to low profitability. This market is served by specialty laboratories or hospitals.) This is an exercise in discontinuity— in disruption of the continuum of care—because for-profit laboratories captured the highest margin business from hospitals years ago. It's like trying to put mismatched pieces of a puzzle together. They don't fit, no matter how hard you try.

Shifting testing among laboratories can cause minor changes in test results, due to differences in methodology or reference ranges. This results in a common practice of repeat testing. The doctor must determine if the change is due to a change in the patient's condition or merely a function of variations in methodology. This duplication of testing is estimated to comprise as much as 20 to 30 percent of all laboratory testing. I argue that it is a cost we cannot afford or should be willing to tolerate.

Laboratorians have always known about this unnecessary repeat testing. Only now are the chickens coming home to roost as others finally understand the clinical and financial impact. Given the new constructs of accountable care organizations (ACOs) and population health management, the onus will be on health care organizations, government payers, and commercial insurance carriers to control the unnecessary cost of duplication. The only logical solution is for the hospital to be the provider of laboratory services across the continuum—the de facto primary laboratory. The national laboratories would (or should) go back to their historical and more appropriate role as reference laboratories for hospitals. This would also put a stop to the insanity of national laboratories competing with their wholesale clients in the retail business!

The third quadrant of the balanced scorecard is efficiency. Like the others before it, efficiency favors hospitals over large national laboratories. Every hospital has sunk costs in its laboratory. It is an essential diagnostic service comprising as much as 75 percent of the medical record. Once a health system has invested in the facilities, equipment, information technology, and staff to serve the inpatient population, expansion to serve others in the community is a logical next step. Most laboratories have considerable spare capacity (upwards of 50 percent) as a result of ever-increasing instrument throughput and automation. Why not leverage that capacity and sunk cost to drive new revenues for the health system? In turn, utilization of spare capacity with additional volume lowers unit cost. Lastly, there is no downside to additional volume; it is all good. Outreach does not compete with hospital volume. The work is performed at opposite times of day. Inpatient work is done largely in the morning, whereas outreach work is performed on second and third shifts. They are perfectly complementary—they go together like yin and yang, black and white, Mickey and Minnie.

The final quadrant, learning and growth, is an area that is much newer to health care than business. Economic constraints have forced health systems to become more efficient, more outcome-oriented, and more accountable for delivering quantitative results. Responsibility for proactively managing the health of an individual patient or populations across the care continuum and simultaneously maintaining fiscal viability is a relatively new phenomenon. The industry is exploring various constructs such as ACOs, other forms of population health management, per capita payments, virtual integration, etc. William Edmondson summed up the situation nicely in a 2015 article on population health:[4]

"In the next generation of healthcare delivery, providers who limit their sphere of influence to particular segments will lose out to aggregators who build high-performing healthcare systems. As new players enter the market, hospitals and health systems will need to redefine the scope and breadth of services. This adjustment will require a fresh reboot of strategic and tactical orientation that will reshape the healthcare enterprise."

The jury is still out on the best solution(s), but the pace of change is faster than a Lamborghini. That race car can only stay in the race if it has continuous GPS coverage to map its direction and a full cockpit crew to keep all parts humming. A fragmented or less-than-fully-functional delivery model will not make it past the first lap.

Here are some concepts that the laboratory industry is learning to provide the highest quality of care at the lowest cost:

- Teaching doctors to order the right laboratory test in the right sequence at the right time.
- Finding instances of over- or under-utilization and providing education to prevent future recurrences.
- Identifying patients who might be at risk for developing disease (such as diabetes, by detecting undiagnosed high blood sugars).
- Pinpointing patients who may not be compliant with treatment protocols or whose disease is not being managed proactively.
- Providing laboratory reports that are easily understandable by patients who then can take some accountability for managing their own health.
- Eliminating the fragmentation of laboratory services across the continuum of care (hospital, physician office, long-term care facility, medical home) by providing an integrated service from one local or regional laboratory.

These changes are being driven by the inescapable fact that health care costs are rising at an unsustainable rate for individuals, companies, and society. This will foster an unprecedented pace of learning and growth for all involved in our industry.

CHAPTER SUMMARY

Outreach makes sense from all four aspects of a balanced scorecard:

1. **Finance**: Economies of scale can lower unit costs by up to 50 percent; the business generates 30 percent operating margins on average and can double every five years.

2. **Efficiency**: Leverage spare capacity and sunk cost in facilities, equipment, and staff; laboratory is unique in that it is the most scalable of all hospital services.

3. **Customer**: Improved service and test menu along with the benefits of continuity of care.

4. **Learning and Growth**: Provides opportunity to partner with physicians and payers on utilization management and patient outcomes.

Given that hospital laboratories outperform the national laboratories on financial metrics, service, and quality, what is the need for national laboratories? Rather than the rationale for outreach, we should examine the rationale for national laboratories. They exist to drive profits for their shareholders, not to improve health care. We do not need them. Competition with hospitals and systems for routine testing in the local market is unnecessary. It is a redundancy that society cannot afford. Hospitals can recapture their local markets and simplify testing while providing better service and quality. This leaves the national laboratories to go back to their original function as reference laboratories. Disruption and redundancy are eliminated. It is both common sense and the best use of limited resources.

CHAPTER 4

THE BATTLE FOR MARKET SHARE BETWEEN HOSPITALS AND INDEPENDENT LABORATORIES

Why is the laboratory market so important? Because in the US, the laboratory market is a $73 billion industry. The market is highly fragmented, with hospitals making up 63 percent of the revenue and 53 percent of the volume as shown in Figure 4.1 on the following page.[1]

Hospitals currently comprise a higher portion of the revenue (on a relative basis compared to volume), due to a higher fee schedule for hospitals versus independent laboratories. This advantage may be short-lived. The Centers for Medicare and Medicaid Services (CMS) is looking for ways to reduce costs and is moving towards paying all laboratories a market-based average under the proposed Protecting Access to Medicare Act of 2014 (PAMA) rule.[2] The impact of this rule will be discussed later in the chapter. Suffice it to say that hospitals control nearly two-thirds of laboratory revenue today, and hospital-based outreach programs continue to grab market share away from independent laboratories. This chapter will describe market segments with a focus on the physician office market, as well as the dynamics and competitive landscape of the laboratory industry.

▶ Hospitals control nearly two-thirds of laboratory revenue today. Hospital-based outreach programs continue to grab market share away from independent laboratories.

MARKET SEGMENTS
The industry is broken out by type of testing into five segments:
- Routine (54 percent)
- Anatomic pathology (26 percent)
- Molecular and esoteric (10 percent)
- Immunology (7 percent)
- Drugs (2 percent)

Laboratory Industry Revenue by Facility Type 2012

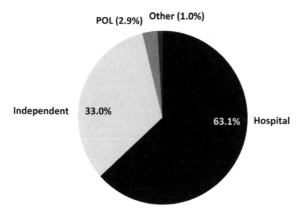

Source: G2 Intelligence, Truven Health Analytics

Laboratory Industry Test Volume (Non-Waived) by Facility Type 2012

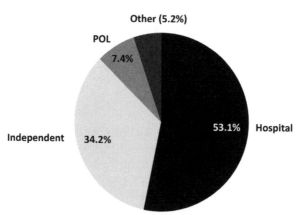

Source: G2 Intelligence, CMS CLIA Oscar Database

From G2 Intelligence U.S. Clinical Laboratory and Pathology Testing 2013-2015: Market Analysis, Trends, and Forecasts. Copyright 2013 by G2 Intelligence. Reprinted with permission.

FIGURE 4.1: LABORATORY INDUSTRY REVENUE AND TEST VOLUME

Hospitals perform routine clinical laboratory testing and pathology along with a small portion of the other, more specialized testing. The majority of the specialized testing (molecular, genetics, and other esoteric testing) is performed by reference laboratories, of which Quest Diagnostics (Quest), LabCorp, and Bio-Reference Laboratories are the largest. Esoteric or highly specialized testing is lower volume but higher margin work.

> Quest and LabCorp couldn't resist the opportunity to capture the routine testing market. Hospitals didn't fight back until the 1970s and 1980s. It was easy to pretend that there was no conflict of interest between being a reference laboratory for hospitals and competing for physician office work in their own, local market. Thus began the "mother of all wars"—the battle for market share between hospitals and independent laboratories.

Ironically, these laboratories were, at one time, pure reference laboratories serving hospitals and smaller independent laboratories. The growth rate of specialized testing (up to 20 to 30 percent annually) greatly surpassed routine testing at less than five percent. Yet Quest and LabCorp couldn't resist the opportunity to capture the routine testing market. So what if it meant that they would compete with their hospital clients? They wanted it all. And hospitals did not fight back until the growth of outreach programs in the 1970s and 1980s (as described in Chapter 1). It was easy to pretend that there was no conflict of interest between being a reference laboratory for hospitals and competing with hospitals for physician office work in their own, local market. Thus began the "mother of all wars"—the battle for market share between hospitals and independent laboratories.

Another way to look at market segments is by origin of testing:

- Physician office
- Long-term care facilities
- Hospitals
- Direct access by patients

This book focuses on the physician office market, which makes up 61 percent of the total. It is my obligation to point out a pitfall in today's market regarding undesirability of long-term care facilities as outreach targets. Increasingly, hospital-based outreach programs are proud of gobbling up nursing home and other extended care facilities as clients. Why? It's because they are easy: no one else wants their business. National and regional independent laboratories dumped that segment years ago because it was unprofitable and high maintenance. There are a small number of dedicated long-term care companies that offer both laboratory and imaging services, but they are fewer and fewer. Many have gone out of business or have been unable to sell the business to another company. At best, a long-term care facility will have a five percent margin, and that's assuming they do everything well. Compare that to a margin of 50 percent for the physician office market. It doesn't take long to figure out where to spend your money.

▶ At best, a long-term care facility will have a five percent margin, assuming they do everything well. That's compared to a margin of 50 percent for the physician office market. It doesn't take long to figure out where to spend your money.

Ignoring this advice can be costly. We worked with a large health system on the West Coast for many years. We provided strategic guidance on outreach and consolidation and helped the organization manage and grow its physician office business. Previously, the system had acquired a multi-million dollar nursing home business that was a drag on its operation and profitability. We recommended the system exit this segment, actually advising them to sell this segment three times over a period of ten years. Our client was in denial about the impact on its business, and kept asking the question to see if we would give a different answer. The system built an offsite core laboratory to support a volume that was one-third larger than it needed without the nursing home business and sold the outreach business a couple of years later due to poor profitability.

A good friend and sales mentor, Tom Searcy, founder of Hunt Big Sales, has a perfect question for me when I am in denial about something that is painfully obvious to him, "What are you pretending you don't know?" It's human nature to deny things that we don't want to hear, but to do so repeatedly and ignore good advice can be fatal.

Note that the one exception to the rule of avoiding this market segment is that every hospital or system has extended care facilities that are important referral sources for the hospital. Limit your business to those facilities that are strategic, and walk away from the rest.

ANALYTICS

We have never seen a market without potential. But how do you determine the value of a market to know if it is a worthwhile target? Some have used a population-based methodology for valuing the market. We do not consider this to be a valid methodology, because of the recent trend of hospitals employing physicians. A physician employed by one hospital/system is not likely to refer his or her laboratory work to a competitive hospital/system. We believe that a more valid and detailed analysis of market potential is constructed by looking at the number of physicians, specifically the number of employed, affiliated, and independent physicians in the market at large.

Employed and affiliated physicians make up what is commonly called the "inreach" market. They are differentiated from physicians that are in the market at large (true outreach) and have no ties to a hospital. Because of their association with a hospital or system, employed and affiliated doctors are much more likely to refer their laboratory work to the hospital laboratory. This inreach market has grown considerably, as more physicians (currently estimated at 65 percent of the total) have become employed by hospitals over the last few years. Figure 4.2 visualizes this shift in the relative size of the inreach and outreach markets.

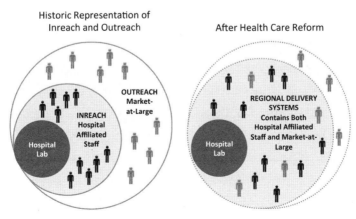

FIGURE 4.2: EVOLUTION OF INREACH VS. OUTREACH MARKETS

The calculation of market potential is based on the number of doctors and the average annual revenue per practice by physician specialty. All doctors are not created equal when it comes to laboratory ordering practices. The highest laboratory users by specialty are general/family practice, internal medicine, and obstetrics/gynecology physicians. Specialists, pediatricians, and surgeons order fewer laboratory tests per patient.

When looking at the market at large, physicians employed by competitor hospitals are considered "unobtainable" and are subtracted from the total. An example of a typical market analysis is shown in Table 4.1.

TABLE 4.1: EXAMPLE MARKET ANALYSIS

Revenue Segment	Current Total Revenue Annual Net Revenue	Percent Distribution	Market Projection[1] Annual Net Revenue	Percent Distribution	Percent Market Share
Employed Physicians	$10,651,561	56.8%	$14,194,340	15.4%	75.0%
Affiliated Physicians	$4,212,976	22.5%	$33,359,944	36.2%	12.6%
Market-at-Large Physicians	2,823,138	15.1%	$44,526,219	48.4%	6.3%
Subtotal	$17,687,675	94.3%	$92,080,503	100.0%	19.2%
Excluded Physicians[2]	$1,068,368	5.7%			
TOTAL	$18,756,043	100.0%			

[1] XYZ Health Systems physicians are non-obtainable business and not included in the market projection.
[2] Not included above – emergency physicians, surgeons, etc.

From this analysis, the next step would be to evaluate different sales assumptions such as the percent share that can be expected over time for the employed/affiliated and market-at-large physicians. For example, it might be reasonable to capture 75 percent of the employed affiliated market and 10 percent of the market at large over five years. This provides a starting point or a range for sales/revenue projections. These assumptions are heavily dependent on the competitive landscape and are best made by a professional sales manager.

GROWTH RATE

There are three trends that will have a positive, material impact on laboratory volume over the next decade:

- New volume will be generated from the millions of Americans that now have access to health care as a result of the Affordable Care Act (up to 30 million new subscribers).
- The population is aging. The first of the Baby Boomers are now retiring. Studies have shown that older patients have five times more laboratory testing than younger patients.
- We continue to see the ongoing development and affordability of new tests.

One may ask about the impact of utilization management on the growth of laboratory testing. While there may be some slowing of the trends above, I don't believe utilization management is sufficient to offset these positive trends. Contrary to popular belief, it is possible that proper utilization management might actually *increase* volume. We may find that many laboratory tests are underutilized, especially in the context of outcomes related to research and the central part that laboratory testing plays in health care decisions.

SUCCESS FACTORS

Looking at the market in the context of strengths and weaknesses is important for hospital executives. Those of us in health care tend to think that quality is what differentiates one laboratory from another and that hospital-based laboratories can prevail over national competitors on their quality reputation. Nothing is further from the truth. Physicians assume that the quality of testing is equivalent. Services are what differentiate laboratories for physicians: turnaround time, customer service, and billing (or the lack of patient complaints about billing). Our market research identifies strengths and weaknesses from the perception of hospital-based outreach programs.

First, the strengths as shown in Figure 4.3 on the following page.

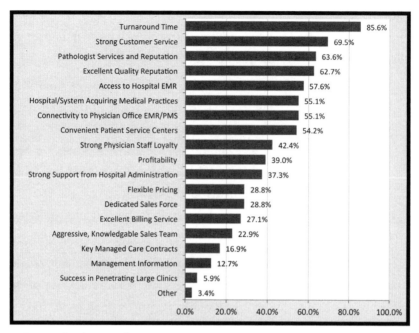

Source: Chi Solutions, 13th Comprehensive National Laboratory Outreach Survey, June 2014.

FIGURE 4.3: HOSPITAL-BASED OUTREACH PROGRAM STRENGTHS

Turnaround time, customer service, interaction with pathologists, quality, and access to the hospital EMR are the top five strengths. Note that all of these, except quality, revolve around the user-friendliness of the laboratory: responsiveness, ease of reaching a pathologist for consultation or questions, and integration of the medical record.

Outreach program weaknesses are identified and shown in Figure 4.4: inadequate budget (more pressure to reduce costs versus generate new revenue), lack of competitive or responsive IT, billing, pricing, and sales.

Although the order of these top five trends varies, the trends themselves have been the same for 15 years with one exception: the pressure to reduce costs has never been so prevalent. How telling is it that hospitals starved for revenue are so focused on cost reduction that they are blind to new revenue opportunities? They can't see the forest for the trees. They have given up on revenue as if it were outdated or, worse, dead.

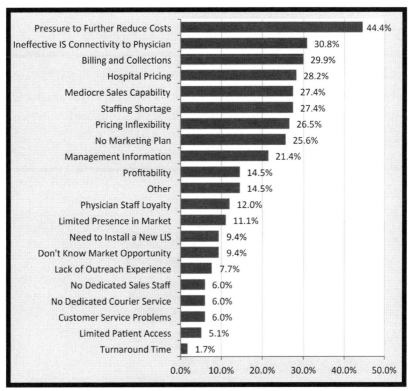

Source: Chi Solutions, 13th Comprehensive National Laboratory
Outreach Survey, June 2014.

FIGURE 4.4: HOSPITAL-BASED OUTREACH PROGRAM WEAKNESSES

▶ The trends have been the same for 15 years with one exception: the pressure to reduce costs has never been so prevalent. Hospitals starved for revenue are so focused on cost reduction that they are blind to new revenue opportunities. They have given up on revenue as if it were outdated or, worse, dead.

PROFITABILITY TRENDS

Cost reductions are rampant across the health care sector—and specifically, in the laboratory industry—in hospital and independent laboratories alike. No one is immune. We're all familiar with ongoing reductions in hospitals, but the independent laboratory sector has been hit just as hard. Both Quest and LabCorp have been undergoing aggressive corporate restructuring to achieve cost savings in the range of $250 million to $500 million.

Revenue is the next focus and perhaps the most impactful issue today. Figure 4.5 demonstrates a downward slide in net revenue per test over the last couple of years consistent with a story of declining reimbursements in health care.

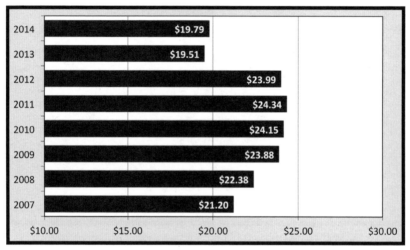

Source: Chi Solutions, 14th Comprehensive National Laboratory Outreach Survey, August 2015.

FIGURE 4.5: AVERAGE OUTREACH NET REVENUE PER TEST BY FISCAL YEAR

At $19.79 per test, hospitals are paid 36 percent more than Quest and LabCorp, at $14.65 and $14.52, respectively. Hospitals are currently reimbursed on a different, higher fee schedule than independent laboratories, based on the assumption that hospitals have higher operational costs. However, this higher cost argument only makes sense for hospital inpatients, since the hospital is required to staff 24/7 to take care of acutely ill patients. The argument does not hold up for hospital outpatients or outreach patients, because these specimens are treated like any commercial laboratory. Testing can be done overnight and resulted by the following morning.

▶ At $19.79 per test, hospitals are paid 36 percent more than Quest and LabCorp at $14.65 and $14.52, respectively. Hospitals are currently reimbursed on a different, higher fee schedule than independent laboratories based on the assumption that hospitals have a higher cost of operations. This favorable reimbursement for hospitals is not founded nor is it likely sustainable.

I have been the proverbial "canary in the coal mine" about reimbursement for hospital-based outreach for years. The favorable reimbursement for hospitals is not founded, nor is it likely sustainable. The time of reckoning is near. Deep discounts given by LabCorp and Quest to private payers in order to secure exclusive agreements have eroded fees over time. The market is now upside down. The U.S. government, once considered the lowest payer, has become the highest payer. CMS has finally figured this out and, as noted previously, is exploring cost reduction via a proposed PAMA rule that would pay all laboratories according to a market-based average of private payers.

Conceptually, I support the concept of a market-based approach to fees, thereby creating a more level playing field. It's the process that's flawed. Hospital laboratories are excluded from submitting data to determine market rates, as are more than 50 percent of independent laboratories and 90 percent of physician office laboratories (POLs). Data will be heavily weighted (50 percent) from the largest five laboratories. And do you think it is a coincidence that these very laboratories are the ones that have engaged in heavy discounting?

▶ The impact of a hospital move to a standardized fee schedule for all clinical laboratories will be deep. Take that 6 percent and add another 36 percent that hospitals are currently paid above independent laboratories and you have a whopping 42 percent.

Laboratory Economics estimates that the difference between private payer and Medicare rates for independent laboratories is approximately 6.4 percent.[3] According to CMS, the proposed rule could result in $360 million in savings for Medicare in 2017 and over $5 billion during the next decade. If this process prevails, rate cuts of 6.7 percent are estimated for 2017, followed by another five percent in 2018, and a final cut of one percent in 2019. Keep in mind that these comparisons are to the clinical laboratory fee schedule for independent laboratories. If hospitals have to move to this standardized fee schedule for all clinical laboratories, the impact will be much deeper. Take that 6 percent and add another 36 percent that hospitals are currently paid above independent laboratories and you have a whopping 42 percent.

At this writing, it is unclear whether the proposed rule will be implemented as written or in the desired timeframe. CMS has not met is own timeline for specifications on how to submit data. There is a veritable backlash in the industry about skewed data collection. National laboratories are appealing to hospitals and smaller laboratories to overwhelm CMS and the legislative branch with unfavorable comments during the November 2015 comment period. Therein lies the irony: the large national laboratories need their competitors to bail them out from their anti-competitive practices of aggressive discounting.

What will be the impact of PAMA on hospitals? Those that have built substantial outpatient/outreach businesses based on favorable hospital rates may be forced to sell to the very laboratories that created the problem (i.e., LabCorp and Quest). The larger the business, the more difficult it will be to sustain a 36 percent or greater drop in revenue. We estimate that Medicare represents about 35 to 40 percent of the payer mix for hospital outpatients/outreach. Outreach programs that currently bill under the independent laboratory fee schedule will experience, at worst, a slight to modest decrease that is easily sustainable. They will, however, still feel the impact of reduced outpatient reimbursement. Many outreach programs have previously migrated to the independent laboratory fee schedule by choice, so that they have a competitive offering on price. These laboratories will be well-positioned for a gain in market share, as competitors such as outreach programs billing hospital rates, small independents, and POLs exit the market. For further detail on this pricing strategy, refer to the discussion in Chapter 7.

▶ Notwithstanding reductions in reimbursement, health systems will be able to compete with large independent laboratories for the foreseeable future through continued consolidation and aggressive outreach.

From a market trends perspective, the data and our more than 25 years of experience in the outreach business tell us that hospitals can effectively compete and win against the large national laboratories. While the industry is stormy, the national laboratories are hitting much stronger headwinds than hospital-based laboratories. They are losing market share because hospitals offer better service and continuity of testing. Physician employment by hospitals and health systems has further accelerated the shift of outreach work to hospitals. And laboratories of all types have further opportunity to offset reimbursement declines with cost reductions. Notwithstanding reductions in reimbursement, health systems will be able to compete with large independent laboratories for the foreseeable future through continued consolidation and aggressive outreach.

COMPETITIVE LANDSCAPE

Widespread growth of hospital outreach programs has become a major headache for the national and large regional independent laboratories. Outreach, once for only the brave and the few, has become mainstream: 80 percent of hospitals have a laboratory outreach program, and large independent laboratories are their main competitors. The current state of the battle for market share is reflected in the results of Chi's *Fourteenth Comprehensive National Laboratory Outreach Survey.*[4] We will review the market highlights and competitive landscape in this chapter.

> ▶ Widespread growth of hospital outreach programs has become a major headache for the national and large regional independent laboratories. Outreach, once for only the brave and the few, has become mainstream: 80 percent of hospitals have a laboratory outreach program, and large independent laboratories are their main competitors.

Various models exist for outreach today. The most common is a single hospital program (39 percent), followed by system or multiple hospital-based programs (36 percent), and independent laboratories owned by a hospital (nine percent). A small minority (less than 10 percent) have an equity joint venture with an independent laboratory or a pathology group, or some other variation not mentioned above.

The primary competitor of outreach programs is always one of the large national laboratories (Quest or LabCorp) or a regional independent laboratory. For all of the fourteen years of this survey, with one exception, Quest has been identified as the primary competitor due to its size. LabCorp comes in second, with the exception of the year it landed an exclusive contract with United Healthcare, which gave LabCorp a temporary leg up.

TABLE 4.2: PRIMARY OUTREACH PROGRAM COMPETITOR 2012-2014

Laboratory	2012 Respondent Percentage	2013 Respondent Percentage	2014 Respondent Percentage	Trend
Quest Diagnostics	47%	40%	38%	↓
LabCorp	23%	33%	28%	↑
Regional Hospital Outreach Program	10%	12%	16%	↑
Regional Independent Laboratory	13%	11%	9%	↓
Other	7%	4%	9%	↑
Total	100%	100%	100%	

Source: Chi Solutions, 14th Comprehensive National Laboratory Outreach Survey, August 2015.

Regional independent laboratories were in third place after Quest and LabCorp, until the past two years when they were surpassed by regional outreach programs. The distinct shift between regional outreach programs and regional independent laboratories is shown in Figure 4.6. Changes are modest year-over-year. When viewed over multiple years, the reversal is obvious. This shift is important from a market perspective, because it means that outreach programs are growing and bumping into each other rather than regional laboratories.

The next question is how are outreach programs impacted by competitors? The great majority of outreach programs report either holding their own or gaining against national and local competitors, as shown in Figure 4.7. Well less than 20 percent are struggling to maintain market share.

▶ The great majority of outreach programs report either holding their own or gaining against national and local competitors. Less than 20 percent are struggling to maintain market share.

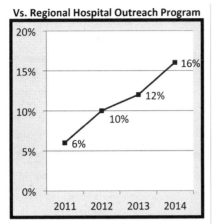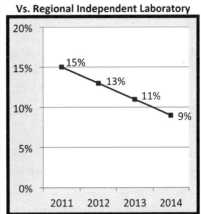

Source: Chi Solutions, 14th Comprehensive National Laboratory Outreach Survey, August 2015.

FIGURE 4.6: MARKET SHARE EXPERIENCE VS. REGIONAL HOSPITAL OUTREACH PROGRAMS
AND REGIONAL INDEPENDENT LABORATORIES

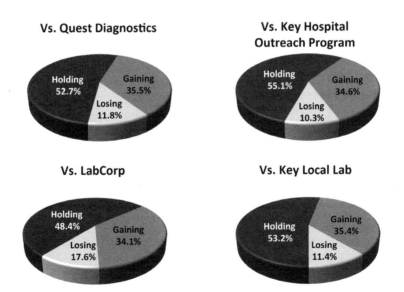

Source: Chi Solutions, 14th Comprehensive National Laboratory
Outreach Survey, August 2015.

FIGURE 4.7: MARKET SHARE EXPERIENCE VS. ALL COMPETITORS

DISRUPTIONS IN THE MARKET

Disruption has now become a common part of the landscape in health care. Everybody is experimenting with different business models—trying to be something new and thinking the grass is greener on the other side. Health providers are becoming payers by developing their own insurance plans. Payers are becoming providers or merging with providers such as Hallmark and Allegheny Health in Pittsburgh, Pennsylvania. In addition, there is a wave of consolidation among providers and payers, with everyone hoping that scale will afford advantage. Both Quest and LabCorp now promote a utilization management offering, trying to insert themselves as a value-added service between providers and payers.

▶ Disruption is a common part of the health care landscape. Everybody is experimenting with different business models—trying to be something new and thinking the grass is greener on the other side.

Notable among shifting business models is the new wave of "partnerships with hospitals" offered by Quest and LabCorp. The national laboratories increasingly see themselves on the outside looking in with the changes in health care. Hospital-based outreach programs and employment of physicians has captured share away from the big laboratories. Quest's 10-K submission for 2014 bemoans the strengthening competitive position of hospitals: affiliation with physicians, greater leverage with health insurers.[5] Outside of acquisitions, organic growth is anemic.

▶ Notable among shifting business models is the new wave of "partnerships with hospitals" offered by Quest and LabCorp. The national laboratories increasingly see themselves on the outside looking in with the changes in health care.

What's a for-profit to do? If you can't beat them, how about joining them? It's called "partnering." Quest CEO Stephen Rusckowski highlights the following approach to restoring growth:

"We plan to grow by pursing strategic partnerships with hospitals and IDNs…We offer a range of solutions, including reference testing, supply chain management, lab management outsourcing, outreach acquisition, other business solutions and joint ventures. We can help our partners to succeed, including by consolidating data and delivering insights, delivering test management solutions to improve care and help control cost and by providing patient-focused programs to enable effective management of care." [6]

The partnership strategy is to offer up to a 20 percent reduction in costs by managing hospital laboratories. Management agreements provide access to the national laboratory's purchasing contracts, eliminate the need for future capital expenditure, and generate improvements in efficiency and productivity by optimizing the testing site. This is a euphemism for shifting work away from the hospital to one of their regional laboratories. And, just in case you didn't guess, the partnership is also a way for the national laboratories to help themselves to hospitals' outreach programs. It is a way for them to get a piece of your business, so beware of the proverbial "wolf in sheep's clothing." Why share when you can have it all—unless you have no appetite for growing your business. Some revenue is better than none, but there are better models out there, such as getting help from an outside party in exchange for paying a fixed fee versus a percentage of revenue. These are summarized in Chapter 8.

▶ The partnership allows the national laboratories to help themselves to hospitals' outreach programs. Beware of the proverbial "wolf in sheep's clothing." Why share when you can have it all?

NEW ENTRANTS

At one time or another over the last decade, point-of-care testing and direct access testing have been identified as potential disruptors. Some declared that point-of-care testing would replace centralized laboratories and that all testing would be performed at the bedside. Direct access testing—allowing patients to order their own tests and become more involved in management of their health—was predicted to fundamentally change medicine. Nonetheless, the impact on the industry for each of these trends has been minor. Point-of-care testing is too expensive to replace automated, centralized laboratories, and the vast majority of patients are not willing to spend their own money on direct access testing.

> ▶ Theranos is a Silicon Valley darling with a $9 billion valuation that markets inexpensive, direct access to consumer laboratory testing through clinics operating inside the pharmacy chain Walgreens. It is a great concept and business model, but lacks credibility from the laboratory industry.

Theranos is a new entrant into the laboratory industry that deserves a detailed discussion. The company is a Silicon Valley darling with a $9 billion valuation that markets inexpensive, direct access to consumer laboratory testing through clinics operating inside the pharmacy chain Walgreens. It is a great concept and business model but lacks credibility from the laboratory industry. Until very recently, Theranos has been able to bypass standard laboratory regulations for introducing new testing. Industry experts have concerns about the accuracy and reproducibility of its secret methodology. CEO and founder Elizabeth Holmes claims the company will revolutionize the laboratory industry with its low cost, less painful blood collection (by finger-stick as opposed to traditional venipuncture) and technology based on very small volume of blood. She has also stretched the truth about how many tests are performed with this new methodology. Recent exposes in the *Wall Street Journal*,[7] the *New York Times*,[8] and multiple laboratory publications have brought the following to light:

- Of the 240 tests performed by Theranos, only 15 were routinely performed with their proprietary methodology. Under pressure from regulators, the FDA restricted the company to performing only a single approved test by its proprietary methodology.

- Physicians and laboratory experts have concerns about the accuracy of testing. Irregularities in handling and processing samples have been noted—irregularities that are outside of acceptable laboratory practice and would cause erroneous results.

- Theranos has had trouble holding on to medical directors and staff, citing concerns about company practices. The inventor of the new methodology committed suicide.

- Finger-stick blood collection is not revolutionary. It has been around for ages and is the standard collection methodology for babies. Elizabeth Holmes has a needle phobia and has marketed the collection of small samples from finger-stick as part of her company's revolution of the laboratory industry.

- The company has bolstered its marketing by announcing deals with multiple companies in addition to Walgreens (Cleveland Clinic, Intermountain Healthcare, Dignity Health, Pfizer, GlaxoSmithKline, and Safeway). Not surprisingly, none of these companies is actively pursuing the relationship. Even Walgreens has placed all plans on hold pending the regulatory approval. Most recently, a *Wall Street Journal* article reported that Walgreens has threatened to terminate the Theranos relationship unless the company can find a quick resolution to its quality problems.[9]

- The company is overhauling its board of directors to include members with industry knowledge. Previously, it was composed of influential politicians.

- Holmes is a quintessential marketer. She raised $400 million in capital by marketing the company as a major disruptor such as Apple. Like Steve Jobs, Holmes is a Stanford dropout and even wears the characteristic black turtleneck to foster the comparison.

- Many questioned the valuation of $9 billion even prior to the recent bad press. Now it is inevitable that it will garner close scrutiny.

This is just the tip of the iceberg. With the FDA and CMS actively investigating the company, more information will come to light. The more appropriate analogy for Theranos might be "the emperor with no clothes" (or maybe just a black turtleneck). I believe the truly disruptive technology for this century will be wearable or implanted devices which are discussed in more detail later in the book.

FRAGMENTATION

 Today, the biggest specter in the laboratory industry and in health care as a whole is fragmentation.

Today, the biggest specter in the laboratory industry and health care as a whole is fragmentation. Everyone is carving out their piece of the pie and making sure their piece is proprietary or protected from the whole. National laboratories are trying to replace hospital laboratories as the main repository of laboratory information. Technology companies charge hospitals multi-millions of dollars to create an electronic medical record that has little to no interoperability. Physicians control most health care costs. Insurance companies make the rules about reimbursement. Hospitals have all the costs, little control over spending, and no control over reimbursement. There is a vacuum in understanding and leadership that can only be filled by hospitals. Their very survival requires it. Laboratory is an enabler and can be the first piece of this puzzle.

CHAPTER SUMMARY

There is plenty for everyone in a laboratory market of $73 billion. Hospitals comprise 63 percent, with the remainder spread across independent laboratories and a minor contingent of physician office laboratories. The largest independent laboratories, Quest and LabCorp, together comprise about 25 percent of the total. Thus, hospitals are sitting in the catbird's seat in a highly fragmented market.

· Of the various types of testing, hospitals perform routine, anatomic pathology, and some of the more common esoteric tests.

· Based on testing origin, the physician office market is the ideal market, making up 61 percent of the total, and is also higher margin work. The long-term care market should be avoided with rare exceptions based on strategic relationships.

· Market potential is calculated by taking the average net revenue by physician specialty times the number of physicians in a particular market. Be sure to exclude physicians employed by unrelated health systems, as they will not likely use a direct competitor.

· The laboratory market is growing as a result of the Affordable Care Act, the aging of the population, and ongoing development of new tests.

· The key driver of success is service.

· Profitability is challenged somewhat by declining reimbursement, but can be offset with increased volume and continuous improvements in cost.

· Eighty percent of hospitals are in outreach today, and the hospitals report that they are gaining or holding their own against the national laboratories.

· Market disruptions are common due to experimentation and exploration of different models. The national laboratories are struggling to maintain share and are promoting "partnerships" with hospitals as a way to stay viable.

Hospitals and independent laboratories are battling for market share in what has been described as the "mother of all wars." With the largest current share of the market and the pivotal role that hospitals play in health care, is it any wonder that the large national laboratories are circling the wagons? They are more scared of hospitals than you are of them; they just won't admit it. It's time to recognize your advantage and go all out and win the war.

CHAPTER 5

STRATEGY

Have you ever wondered about the derivation of the term "copy-cat?"

I never really understood how it started until recently. I am primarily a dog lover, having shared my life with four wonderful dog companions. Cats are literally and figuratively a different kind of animal. They can be totally independent of humans yet are highly interactive with each other, making different trill sounds to communicate with each other. Last year I adopted three cats to help control chipmunks in my garden.

In the winter when there are no chipmunks, the cats live to torment my five-month old puppies. All it takes is one cat to begin the mayhem. One jumps up on the dog crate. Next thing, I look over and all three of them have ganged up on the puppies. The cats lounge around on the floor outside their crate, sit on top of the crate, try to claw the puppies, and provide all manner of torment. One starts and sends out the message—trill, trill—and the others *copy*. Soon, all three of them are doing the exact same thing… being copy-cats! As soon as I let the puppies out, the cats scatter, and the cycle starts again when the dogs are crated.

Just like cats, businesses have a way of copying new tricks or behaviors that seem different. Before you know it, everyone is being a copy-cat, and someone has to break out and try something new. The rest start to follow and the cycle recurs.

But what if you conceived a unique competitive advantage and developed all your company activities around this advantage so that they reinforce each other and make it very difficult to copy? Maybe the investment would be too high. Maybe you might have to move up or down market. Maybe you have to shift from a high cost to a low cost delivery model. Maybe you have to develop a set of interrelated operational practices that are 180 degrees from your current play book. Whatever "it" is, it is a total makeover. Most companies would not have the courage or appetite to undertake a total makeover. Therein lays your competitive advantage.

Michael Porter is my absolute favorite strategist. Many years ago, I read his seminal 1996 *Harvard Business Review* article titled, *What is Strategy?*[1] I have read, re-read, and referred to this article countless times as I've mulled over strategy for both my own company and for my clients. I will use this article as a construct to imagine different future strategic options for laboratories.

Porter's approach to strategy is based on three key principles:[2]

1. **Do not confuse strategy with operational effectiveness**. Companies have been led astray by chasing productivity, quality, efficiency, benchmarking, outsourcing, partnering, change management, lean six sigma, and others. While these activities might improve operational effectiveness and ultimately profitability, they are not sufficient to create meaningful or lasting differences between companies. Each of the operational strategies mentioned above have resulted in a series of endless "copy-cat" improvements. Strategic positioning requires that a company construct activities that are different from rivals or perform similar activities in different ways. Otherwise, differences are temporary—just long enough for your competitor to figure out how to copy it. Then you have to figure out something new all over again. Make your offering different from rivals, not just a better version of the same offering. Deliberately choosing a different set of activities defines a unique value. It is the only way to ensure sustainability.

2. **Combine unique activities that fit together like a puzzle and reinforce each other**. This is the secret to preventing imitation by competitors. Southwest Airlines had to make drastic changes to be profitable with low prices: instituting automatic ticketing, standardizing aircraft to simplify crew training, making frequent and reliable departures, ensuring high aircraft utilization, perfecting short gate turnarounds to fit in more flights per day, and others that will be discussed more in detail shortly. All the pieces "fit" together and reinforce each other, making imitation extremely difficult and unlikely. The more pieces fit together and strengthen the whole, the more difficult it is to copy—and the more likely you can maintain a competitive advantage over time.

3. **A sustainable strategic position requires tradeoffs**. We can't be *all* things to *all* clients. More importantly, some positions, when grouped together, are inconsistent or mutually exclusive. For example, a company can't provide high-end, personalized service like Nordstrom and compete on price.

Porter gives a great example in Southwest Airlines. Southwest built a whole new value proposition of low-cost travel (just slightly higher cost than auto travel but with the speed of air travel). This model was successful because it traded off some of the perks of legacy airlines, such as assigned seats, meals, and baggage transfers to other airlines, for low cost. This strategy has been wildly successful as Southwest has grown to a $19 billion company over 45 years.

Southwest mapped out a totally new and compelling travel proposition that would appeal to business and pleasure travelers alike: a low-cost model that approximated the cost of automobile travel paired with the speed of flying. The airline appealed to the masses because its low-cost model required high volume. Another courageous departure from the norm was that Southwest declared its company philosophy was to have fun! How crazy that seemed compared to the staid, buttoned-down, anti-fun legacy airlines for which mistreating clients was an art form. The Southwest model is shown in Figure 5.1.

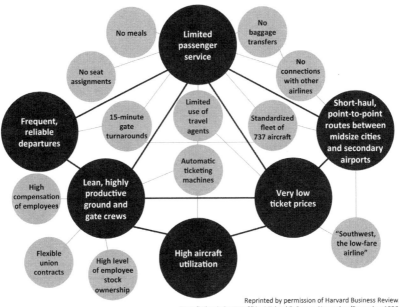

FIGURE 5.1: SOUTHWEST AIRLINES—A LOW-COST PROVIDER

Let's examine Southwest's strategy. According to Porter, the first criterion for outperforming rivals is to establish a difference that can be preserved. Customers must perceive lower cost, greater value, or both. We touched on this approach earlier: performing different activities from competitors or performing similar activities in different ways, thereby creating divergence from the rest of the market. Here are some examples to elucidate this concept:

- The first airline to offer what is now a common place service: online booking to avoid (now defunct) commissions to travel agents.

- Traditional airline hub and spoke systems, designed to get passengers almost anywhere, centered on major airports, contrasted with Southwest's point-to-point system.

- Comfort features of first class, assigned seats, and meals, compared to all coach class, open seating, and peanuts.

- Coordination of schedules and baggage transfer across legacy airlines are absent on Southwest.

- Highly efficient gate turnarounds allow Southwest airplanes to fly more hours and more passengers in a day to compensate for lower prices.

- Standardization of aircraft to the 737 reduces training time, avoids mismatched crews, and boosts maintenance efficiency.

- An employee compensation model that results in labor unions and grievances versus employees seeing themselves as owners.

Individually, none of these activities seem compelling or particularly insightful. However, it is the combination—the inter-relatedness and reinforcement—of the activities that allowed Southwest to develop a sustainable strategic position. How many of us underestimated them initially? I doubt that I was the only one that used to chuckle at the spectacle of employees dressed in shorts acting like cheerleaders, herding all the customers into their boarding lanes like cattle. I could understand the value proposition for personal travel, especially for families, but for business travelers, no way! In time, I heard stories about Southwest's reliability and watched the 15-minute gate turnarounds while I was collecting dust waiting for delayed flights on a legacy airline. Now, I count myself among the converted and fly Southwest regularly for point-to-point destinations in their major airports.

▶ The biggest danger is *not* following Porter's advice and doing what everybody else is doing, what Porter calls "competitive convergence." Companies imitate one another in a type of herd behavior, each assuming rivals know something they do not.

The biggest danger for us is *not* following Porter's advice and doing what everybody else is doing—what Porter calls "competitive convergence." In doing so, "companies imitate one another in a type of herd behavior, each assuming rivals know something they do not."[3]

The second biggest danger in using Porter's approach is going only halfway, what strategists call "straddling." This is a form of imitation that copies some aspects of a competitor's position while trying to maintain the current position.

Years ago, Continental tried to imitate Southwest's position on select point-to-point routes. The new service, called "Continental Lite," had some of the characteristics of Southwest: lower fares, no meals, no first class service, increased departure frequency, and shortened gate turnarounds. But Continental maintained inefficiencies by continuing to use travel agents, a variety of planes, seat assignments, and baggage transfer to other airlines. They also tried to maintain their offering as a full-service airline on other routes. This caused market confusion; the company attempted to deliver two inconsistent strategies simultaneously.

The result was a disaster. The company lost hundreds of millions of dollars and the CEO was canned, all because of straddling. It could not afford to compete on price without overhauling its costs. This story highlights the need to make tough decisions, what Porter calls "trade-offs." This is the second key lesson in strategic positioning. Deciding what *not* to do is just as important as deciding what to do.

The third and final strategic positioning lesson from Porter is "fit." Southwest's strategy was more than a set of unrelated activities; it was a system of interrelated activities that "fit" together like a puzzle. The pieces of the puzzle interlock and reinforce each other. It brings to mind the saying, "The whole is greater than the sum of its parts." Fit is a critical component of competitive advantage, because it becomes infinitely harder for a rival to imitate a system of interlocking, reinforcing activities.

APPLYING PORTER'S LESSONS

So how do we apply Porter's three positioning concepts of establishing a difference that can be preserved, making trade-offs, and ensuring fit to the laboratory market? How can hospital laboratories establish a position that differentiates them from the independent laboratories, ensures fit, and makes imitation impossible? I see three possible strategic positions.

The first position is analogous to Southwest: the low-cost laboratory, as shown in Figure 5.2.

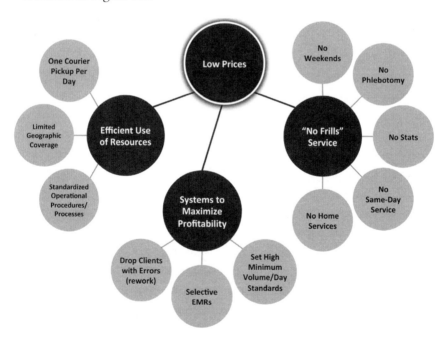

FIGURE 5.2: LOW-COST LAB VALUE PROPOSITION

I envision three interrelated activities to drive costs down:

- "No frills" service
- Efficient use of resources
- Systems to maximize profitability

"No frills" service is a necessary trade-off for low prices. A full-service laboratory has multiple access points: patient service centers, phlebotomists embedded in physician practices, and home phlebotomy. All phlebotomy services are eliminated in the low-cost laboratory. If you want service, go to the Nordstrom of the laboratory world. The low-cost laboratory uses other companies' resources to draw blood, such as medical assistants in physician offices or visiting nurses for home-bound patients. To maximize efficiency, specimens are picked up by couriers or, perhaps, drones, once per day (compared to more frequent pickups by couriers in the full-service laboratory). Geographic coverage is limited. Stat or same-day services are not available. The laboratory is not a 24/7 operation; testing is performed on the third shift Monday through Friday.

The laboratory is a lean, mean production machine, totally standardized and automated. Because all functions are automated, except reviewing and releasing abnormal results, staffing is at an all-time minimum and productivity is logarithmically higher than in traditional laboratories. The few medical technologists employed are highly compensated and are shareholders to ensure alignment with company priorities. Profitability is enhanced by doing business with only high-volume clients. Those that make errors or cause rework, such as submitting specimens that are not barcoded or with labels askew, are fired. Clients are selected using the 80/20 rule: the laboratory selects the 20 percent of the clients that comprise 80 percent of the volume in a particular market. The low-cost laboratory is a feared negotiator, constantly driving down costs with suppliers. I could go on, but you get the gist: clear, simple, consistent, reinforcing, and interlocking activities.

The second position, the continuum of care laboratory, has a totally different value proposition, as shown in Figure 5.3.

It is a high service model and, therefore, more costly. The laboratory provides services to all market segments within a defined geography. It serves the traditional market segments of the hospital (inpatient and outpatient) and physician offices. Whereas long-term care and medical homes would be avoided in traditional models, they are a critical part of the continuum of care model. The direct cost of providing this high level of service up front is no longer important. The view is longer-term, based on outcomes of better health and saving money over the life of the population.

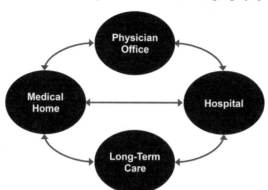

Serve all market segments within a defined geography.

- Complete history—better patient management
- Eliminate duplicate testing

FIGURE 5.3: CONTINUUM OF CARE VALUE PROPOSITION

The continuum of care model is more proactive. Health providers view the whole patient record across all segments simultaneously. Health is managed over time. Disease is diagnosed and treated earlier. There is no need for repeat testing (a common practice today when results from different laboratories vary), because laboratory results are comparable across the continuum. All testing is performed in the same laboratory with the same equipment, methodologies, and reference ranges. I have not been able to find a reference for the amount of duplicate testing in our current model. I have heard anecdotes that repeat testing may comprise as much as 30 percent of all testing. Not all of this repeat testing is due to changing laboratories. Some occurs through arcane practices of standing orders, which are slowly being eliminated. Nonetheless, the continuum of care model would eliminate all redundant testing.

The third position is the "smart" laboratory, as shown in Figure 5.4. The "smart" laboratory works with providers as a partner in managing health. It does this primarily through a high-touch and high-tech approach. The "smart" laboratory is able to proactively identify patients at risk for disease or patients whose disease is not well-managed and thereby reduce the likelihood of bad outcomes and downstream cost. Pathologists and other laboratory professionals participate in rounds of patient care teams comprised of specialists in all aspects of the patient's care. These laboratory professionals educate primary care and specialist physicians and guide them in the proper selection and sequencing of tests in complicated cases.

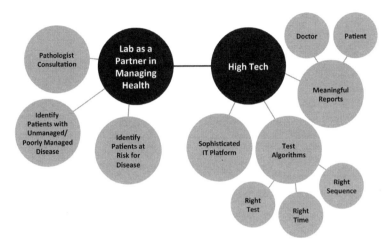

More sophisticated model—two related but separate activities.

FIGURE 5.4: "SMART" LAB VALUE PROPOSITION

The high-tech part of the equation is based on a sophisticated information technology (IT) platform that provides test algorithms to guide physicians to order the right test in the right sequence at the right time. The "smart" laboratory also provides more meaningful reports for physicians and patients. Decisions are made more quickly and with confidence. The result is faster diagnosis/treatment and better patient outcomes.

Looking back at the three models, each has a different value proposition and varying levels of fit and sophistication. I see the "smart" laboratory as the most differentiated and sophisticated because it has two related but separate values: high-tech and high-touch. The continuum of care model as described is the easiest to copy, although it is difficult to implement because of the different requirements for the four different market segments (hospital, physician office, long-term care, and medical home). The low-cost laboratory is in between; it requires many more trade-offs than the other models and sustainability will largely be determined by the ability to eke out a margin.

CHAPTER SUMMARY

Which is the best model for the future? There is so much disruption in health care that it is impossible to predict. Two or more models may (and often do) exist simultaneously in any given market at any time. The key is to stake out your position and follow Porter's rules:

1. Construct unique activities that are different from your competition or are performed in such a way to make your competition irrelevant.

2. Limit activities which do not support your value proposition; avoid "straddling" by making the necessary trade-offs.

3. Make the pieces "fit" together like a puzzle so that they support and reinforce each other. The position will be as strong as the strongest link.

CHAPTER 6

OPERATIONAL INFRASTRUCTURE

The beauty of outreach is that you already have most of the infrastructure needed to develop a thriving business. You already have the facilities, laboratory equipment, automation, and staff for a going concern. You already have a lot of spare capacity, by a factor of 100 percent or more.

That's right. Most laboratories can double their volume without exhausting capacity. You get the picture. You already have most of what you need, so what's stopping you? The devil is often in the details—you don't know exactly what to do. And how do you make sure that you get it right, out of the gate? What is the risk of failure? This is what we will review in this chapter.

Let's begin with the end in mind and draw a picture of a large, successful outreach program. We don't want the average—the run of the mill, mom-and-pop business—we want something to provide material margin for your hospital or system. Here's the prototype of laboratory as an economic engine:

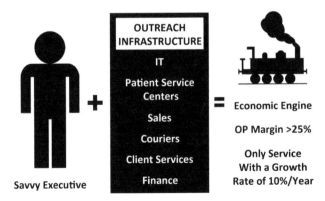

FIGURE 6.1: LABORATORY AS AN ECONOMIC ENGINE

Here's the recipe. Start with a savvy hospital executive. Add in some infrastructure of IT, patient service centers (PSCs), sales, couriers, client services, and finance, and you get a new economic engine for your hospital or health system. This engine is the only hospital service that enjoys a 25 percent operating margin and a year–over–year growth rate of over 10 percent.

▶ We have seen examples of laboratories that comprise only five percent of hospital costs generating 50 percent of hospital earnings before appreciation, taxes, and amortization (EBITDA). Outreach is the gift that keeps on giving—the proverbial goose that lays the golden egg.

The following are defining characteristics of a large ($50 million) outreach program, as compiled from a recent Chi presentation at the 2015 G2 Intelligence Lab Revolution conference and our general experience:

- Substantial in size: $50 million or larger.
- Operating margin of $12.5 million (25 percent).
- Growth rate in excess of 10 percent per year.
- Seventy-five percent of business comes from what we call "inreach," physicians affiliated with the organization.
- The remaining 25 percent of the business is true "outreach," coming from independent physicians in the market at large.
- Twenty or more PSCs.
- Operating expenses of $37.5 million, mostly for staff and supplies:
  - More than 15 phlebotomists embedded in physician offices.
  - Thirty-five couriers and 35 vehicles.
  - Five FTEs of dedicated sales and service representatives, managed by a professional sales manager.
  - Other support staff, such as specimen processors and client services.
  - Additional technical staff for added volume.
- Capital outlay of approximately $900,000 per annum.
- Billing systems or services that segregate revenue from the hospital and provide sophisticated management reports.
- Quarterly profit and loss statement, produced by the finance department in collaboration with the laboratory.
- Laboratory is involved in negotiations with managed care contracts and setting outreach pricing.

What is surprising to most hospital executives is that the capital requirement is modest. Most of the investment is in operating expense, and most of that is in FTEs. Why is that? It's because you are leveraging your sunk costs in the laboratory you already have for your inpatient operation. There are some upfront costs to get the infrastructure in place, particularly for IT systems, which will result in a loss in Year 1. Beyond that, the capital is for interfaces to physician offices, and that is contingent on securing the business. Programs are usually breakeven and make some margin in Year 2. Financial considerations will be discussed in more detail in the next chapter. The key point is that most of the cost is operating expense, and because of that, there is little long-term risk should the business change.

So, how do you build the necessary infrastructure? I will impart insights that you can only get from an insider. My intention is not to describe all the detailed operational requirements, but more to share hard-learned perspectives for executives from an experienced operator.

INFORMATION TECHNOLOGY

A robust outreach business requires supplemental information technology (IT) software (middleware) that allows doctors to order tests and view results in their electronic medical records (EMRs). There are multiple companies that offer good options with a range of functionality and pricing. IT connectivity is often the rate-limiting step for growth. The typical implementation timeline is 6-9 months, so this is a critical step in developing a start-up. Many ongoing businesses get "stuck" at the $10 million mark because of a lack of full IT functionality. Capital-constrained organizations may cede to the temptation of making do with the hospital physician portal provided by Epic, Cerner, and the like. Or, they provide a results-only interface instead of a two-way orders and results interface. Resist this temptation at all costs. Doctors want to order and view laboratory test results integrated into their own EMR in the way that they like to view results and practice their workflow. Anything else is an inconvenience that they will not tolerate.

Beyond functionality, the second biggest obstacle we see is the inability to execute interfaces in a timely manner to bring on new practices. One of our long-term clients had an extreme example of IT as a bottleneck instead of an enabler. Together, we built a $20 million business for this three-hospital system in the Southeast. The laboratory had over $1 million in revenue on hold at any given time, pending completion of interfaces. We tried everything to break the log-jam, but nothing seemed to work. Finally, we developed a report that showed how much money the client was losing each month as a result of the inability to execute interfaces in a timely manner. We shamelessly embarrassed them into taking action, presenting our findings religiously and as often as possible to any executive willing to listen.

The outreach programs that do the best have their own dedicated IT resources. Laboratories dependent upon hospital IT resources often go to the back of a very long line of projects. It is impossible for these laboratories to be competitive when Quest or LabCorp turn interfaces around in six weeks. The aforementioned client had an interface turn-around of 10 times that of their competitors. Hmm… do you think they had trouble meeting their sales numbers?

Another of our clients did not have a competitive offering for IT. It provided a results-only interface and wondered why it couldn't grow more quickly. We worked together to develop a five-year financial plan showing growth of $10 million over five years, and we told the client that achieving this level of growth had certain dependencies for sales, service, and connectivity (two-way orders and results interface, ability to connect to physician EMRs).

As a small, independent hospital, it was focused on revenue, but kept forgetting its commitment to IT. First, the hospital wanted to try to upgrade using its current vendor (which we recommended against). Next, a state-wide health information exchange was the answer, until the hospital realized (after wasting 18 months) that the exchange only stored results and lacked an ordering functionality. Lastly, after two years, when they were hopelessly behind on revenue, the client proclaimed that IT wasn't the problem, it was us—our sales team was not up to par! This hospital was totally in denial. Thankfully, it merged into a health system with a large existing outreach program that had the Cadillac of laboratory connectivity offerings, and we agreed to exit.

This is a case in point of what I referenced earlier: the tendency to repurpose existing or planned IT. This is crazy! Hospitals are spending hundreds of millions on new EMRs, yet they won't invest $50,000 to $250,000 for a product that will drive $10 million in new revenue. The moral of these stories is that once you know something, you can't pretend that you don't know it. Don't cut corners on infrastructure. Doing this will jeopardize your base business and stymie future growth.

> ▶ The moral of these stories is that once you know something, you can't pretend that you don't know it. Don't cut corners on infrastructure. Doing this will jeopardize your base business and stymie future growth.

While this section is short, don't confuse length with importance. IT is always in the top five weaknesses identified by outreach programs when Chi performs its annual *Comprehensive National Laboratory Outreach Survey*.[1] We've been conducting this survey for fourteen years now, and the story stays the same.

PATIENT ACCESS

Taking a process point of view, we start with specimen collection and points of patient access. The most efficient and profitable method is to use what I call OPR ("Other People's Resources") to draw your specimens. Medical assistants and nurses collect specimens as a routine part of the physician's practice. Laboratory couriers pick up specimens and deliver them to the laboratory for testing. OPR is a beautiful thing.

PSCs are the second best entry point for patients to access your services. Multiple access points from within your market are required by many managed care contracts. PSCs are the most efficient and most profitable way to offer phlebotomy, provided that they are strategically located in or adjacent to high-volume physician clients. Twenty-five to thirty patients per phlebotomist per business day are required to make a PSC profitable. Make your sales representatives do a pro forma to justify a new PSC.

A well-run PSC should have a margin of 75 percent or more. If it does not meet your margin criteria within six months, give your sales representatives three months to achieve volume targets. If they fail, close the PSC. Do not believe it when they tell you that it will get better over time. Make sure your lease is exclusive, so that competitors cannot open up a competing PSC in your building. You would be amazed at how many hospital-owned medical office buildings have exclusive contracts with Quest Diagnostics or LabCorp. The hospital has given away the farm for ten, fifteen, or twenty years and can't get the business from their owned and affiliated doctors.

I referenced some of the requirements of PSCs in an earlier chapter:

- Convenient locations with directions.
- Extended hours (early morning and evening hours during week-days and Saturday mornings; do not close for lunch).
- Offer appointments by telephone or web.
- A streamlined registration process. Do not torture patients with asking dozens of questions required for a full hospital registration. Find a way to do a "mini-registration" requiring only the neces-sary information to process a laboratory claim.
- Ensure a 15-minute turnaround time—even offer a guarantee to differentiate yourself from competitors.

The next method of specimen collection is embedding a laboratory phlebotomist in a physician's practice. This practice was started by the national laboratories and has become commonplace in the last 10 years. It is sometimes a necessary evil to winning the business. Used appropri-ately and managed for profitability and compliance, this practice can help grow top line revenue, especially with larger group practices. However, this is always a third choice, because it is rare for a doctor's office phlebotomist to achieve the same volumes and efficiency per day as a PSC phlebotomist. In addition, there are strict anti-kickback statutes restricting the activities of the phlebotomist exclusively to laborato-ry-related work. It is difficult to ensure that the phlebotomist is not engaged in any other office activities. For this reason, physician office phlebotomists are prohibited in New York, California, and, most recently, Florida. Lastly, steer clear of renting space in a physician's office for a pseudo-PSC. These are borderline-compliant and rarely garner addi-tional volume from outside the practice.

COURIERS

If you have an established business, a self-managed courier service provides the best service, cost, and efficiency. Start-up operations often use outsourced couriers initially and then transition the business over time. This is a classic make-versus-buy-decision and should be assessed periodically. Most laboratories have a minor, ongoing component of outsourced services to cover off hours and weekends.

Underestimate the importance of couriers at your peril. I have seen physician offices switch laboratories because of their allegiance to a courier. Consider them ambassadors for your business, and make sure that they are professional in dress and manner. Ensure that they have the necessary technology to track specimens (similar to UPS). Losing a specimen is the absolute worst error for a laboratory. Unlike packages, many patient specimens such as tissue biopsies cannot be recollected and are critical for diagnosis or treatment.

LABORATORY OPERATIONS

What is the impact of all this new volume on laboratory operations? There are fewer negative impacts than you might expect, because outreach is perfectly complimentary to hospital business. The vast majority of laboratory testing for hospital inpatients is performed in the early morning hours. Outreach work arrives by courier starting in the afternoon and continues through the evening, with the last courier drop-off at 10:00 or 11:00 p.m. Testing is performed overnight and results sent to physicians prior to business hours the next morning.

Hospital and outreach businesses are the perfect pair; they go together like yin and yang, peanut butter and jelly, Mickey and Minnie. Of course, there are occasional wrinkles. Staffing for front-end specimen processing has to be monitored by volume and by hour of day to avoid bottlenecks. Knowledge of lean manufacturing practices is an asset. Outreach is the perfect antidote to spare capacity in your laboratory. You've built a lean, mean production machine with high-tech equipment and automation that functions at less than half capacity for all but a few hours of the day without outreach. How crazy is that?

The staffing impact of outreach is seen primarily among the support staff (phlebotomists, couriers, specimen management, client services, billing, and IT). Few technical staff members are needed, except in highly manual disciplines like microbiology and cytology. Table 6.1 gives you an idea of the range of full time equivalents (FTEs) for businesses of different sizes.

TABLE 6.1: RANGE OF OUTREACH PROGRAM FTES FOR A $10 MILLION TO $50 MILLION BUSINESS

	Program Size		
Full-Time Equivalents	**$10 Million**	**$25 Million**	**$50 Million**
Technologist	4.0	10.0	10.0
Non-Technical (Specimen Accessioning/Customer Service)	5.0	12.0	23.0
Phlebotomist	18.0	43.0	86.0
Courier	8.0	18.0	36.0
Information Technology Analyst	3.0	4.0	5.0
Vice President	1.0	1.0	1.0
Outreach Program Manager	1.0	1.0	1.0
Marketing Manager	1.0	1.0	1.0
Sales Representatives	2.0	5.0	10.0
Field Service Representatives	1.0	3.0	5.0
Finance Manager	1.0	1.0	1.0
Total FTEs	**45.0**	**99.0**	**179.0**

The staffing component of outreach may negatively impact how your laboratory is viewed by most benchmarking services. Because outreach is heavy on support staff, your laboratory costs will appear higher than those of laboratories without outreach. Paradoxically, your laboratory will appear to be a low performer.

Here is a real-life example from one of our clients with a $20 million outreach program. They called me one day in a panic, because the laboratory director was told she had to reduce 20 FTEs in the hospital laboratory. The basis for the decision was a ranking in the 30th percentile for unit cost (where the 100th percentile is the best performer). The analysis was performed by a general consulting firm that did not understand the complexities of the laboratory. We used the exact same data submission and changed only the peer group, comparing this laboratory to other laboratories with comparable outreach volume (greater than 50 percent). Laboratory performance improved by 43 percentiles! The results are shown in Table 6.2.

TABLE 6.2: IMPACT OF BENCHMARKING AGAINST OUTREACH PEER GROUP

Metric	Percentile Performance[1,2]		Comment
	Standard Peer Group	**Outreach Peer Group**	
Unit Cost	30th	73rd	Cost of outreach infrastructure

[1]100th percentile is top performer.
[2]The same lab compared to two different peer groups.

We all want comparisons to be fair, to be grouped with those that are most similar to us. If our peers are not comparable, then benchmarking results are skewed or invalid. This laboratory was not a low performer by any standards. It was a GOOD performer, ranking close to the 75th percentile when benchmarked with a comparable peer group. The first analysis the laboratory received didn't account for the cost of outreach infrastructure (FTEs, space rental, courier vehicles, IT systems, etc.), which is a prerequisite for the laboratory outreach business. When compared with other laboratories in the outreach business, this facility performed in the top third of the peer group.

I'm going to plant a seed that will be explored in the next chapter on financial considerations. None of the hospital-wide benchmarking services factor revenue into the equation. They only measure half of the equation: cost without regard to revenue!

TURNAROUND TIME FOR RESULTS

This is where hospital laboratories have a distinct advantage over large national and regional laboratories. As a 24/7 operation that serves acutely ill patients, hospital laboratories are designed to provide quick turnaround of results. Stat services for the emergency department or intensive care units are provided in less than one hour. Most automated laboratories can turn around routine tests within an hour of two of receipt and report results back the same day. This real-time testing provides a competitive advantage for local hospitals, compared to national or regional laboratories. These laboratories function as third-shift operations, doing large batch testing overnight and reporting results the next day. This will become even more important within the context of managing population health on fixed reimbursements. After all, time is money.

CLIENT SERVICES

It's easy to tell laboratories that have dedicated, sophisticated client services or call centers from those who don't. It's easy to differentiate the harried, no-nonsense technologist who views the call as an interruption to his or her "real" work and the courteous, professional client service staff member that will go out of his or her way to please a customer. You might think this is self-evident, but well more than half of the laboratories we see do not have a dedicated client service department. This is non-negotiable if you want to be in the outreach business. A distinctive client service approach can be a competitive advantage and can also be leveraged to improve service on the inpatient side of the operation.

Below are a few key points to give you the flavor of what is required. This is not rocket science; it is developing a state-of-the-art call center to delight your clients:

- An automated call distribution (ACD) system to monitor call performance and staff productivity.
- Wireless headsets for staff so that they can move away from their desks to perform other functions.
- Software that prominently displays the number and length of time customers are on hold and warns staff if internal benchmarks are exceeded so everyone can log in and reduce wait times.
- Access to laboratory IT, hospital IT, reference laboratories, production schedules, and other information that will allow staff to answer the maximum amount of questions on the first try.
- Ratio of non-technical to technical staff of about 5:1.
- Hours of operation to match your clients, including early evening and Saturday morning.

All outreach infrastructure elements reviewed in this chapter are essential. You cannot skip any steps or take short-cuts. Laboratories have lost clients because of unprofessional phlebotomists, missed courier pickups, inability to provide competitive IT connectivity, test ordering errors, poor turnaround time, billing problems, and lackluster customer service. Think of service as a complex, interdependent chain of events. The service is only as strong as its weakest link. Failure at any point in the chain breaks the connection and the business is lost, usually irreparably.

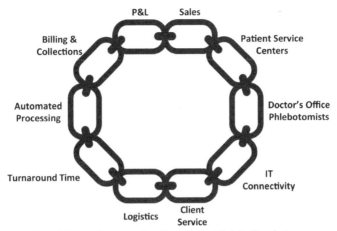

Your lab is only as good as the weakest link in the chain.

FIGURE 6.2: CHAIN LINK OF LABORATORY SERVICES

I discuss insurance contracts, pricing, billing, and P&L in the chapter on financial considerations, and sales and field service in the subsequent chapter.

CHAPTER SUMMARY

You can build a powerful economic engine for your hospital by leveraging the spare capacity of your existing laboratory. Additional infrastructure components are layered on to provide a competitive outreach offering. Building this infrastructure is not particularly difficult, but it is complex because of the myriad of requirements. It requires specialized knowledge and expertise, as well as bandwidth that you may not have in your current organization.

The requirements are exacting. Resist the allure of repurposing existing solutions or going halfway and expecting full results. The business is too competitive. A half-hearted approach will ultimately limit your growth and profitability, as well as damage your reputation.

Think of service as a complex, interdependent chain of events. Unlike strategy, discussed in the last chapter, where the business is as strong as the strongest link, when it comes to service, the business is only as strong as its weakest link. Failure at any point in the chain breaks the connection and the business is lost, usually for good. False starts are deadly. Second chances are rare.

In conclusion, the biggest risk of failure is in trying to make do with what you have or repurposing solutions designed for inpatients. In this highly competitive market, you cannot run a successful outreach business of $50 million like the mom-and-pop corner store. It will not be competitive. It will not make its numbers. It will be considered a failure and reflect poorly on the institution and you. And, all the while, it could have been avoided because you knew better.

CHAPTER 7

FINANCIAL CONSIDERATIONS

While there are many reasons to consider outreach, the most powerful is that outreach can be an economic engine, generating as much as 50 percent of hospital EBITDA from five percent of the costs.

Consider this analogy. The average outreach program is like the old neighborhood "mom-and-pop" hardware store, compared to one of the big box, national chains like Lowe's or Home Depot (depicted in Figure 7.1).

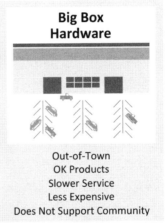

Mom & Pop's Hardware	Big Box Hardware
Local	Out-of-Town
Quality Products	OK Products
Quick Service	Slower Service
Fair Price	Less Expensive
Supports Community	Does Not Support Community

FIGURE 7.1: MOM & POP HARDWARE VS. BIG BOX HARDWARE

In the big picture, the outreach program does not have the scale or sophistication of the national laboratories. It cannot compete on price. It provides quality testing for the community —some would say better than the nationals. It keeps jobs local. It provides faster turnaround time and personalized service. It leverages the sunk investment in facilities, equipment, and staff in the hospital laboratory and lowers the cost of testing overall. It's the only laboratory that does testing across the patient continuum (hospital, extended care facilities, doctor's office, and medical home), not because it's profitable but because it's the right thing to do.

This care continuum is absolutely essential for meeting future challenges, such as utilization and population health management. The hospital laboratory outreach program must be preserved. It is good patient care and good business.

How do you overcome the preconceived ideas, the obstacles, and the risks? In this chapter, we will take a systematic common sense approach to all financial issues and concerns. They are all manageable with the right information and some grit and determination, and include the following components:

- Unit cost
- Contracting
- Pricing
- Reimbursement
- Billing
- Financial transparency
- Performance
- Risk

UNIT COST

One of the big benefits of outreach not mentioned heretofore is the impact of additional volume on unit costs. We all understand the concept of efficiencies of scale. Do you think the volume impact is seen early with modest increases in volume or only much later in the growth curve? Most of us would guess the latter, but, counter intuitively, it's just the opposite.

 Surprisingly, volume impact is seen early with modest increases in volume not only much later in the growth curve.

Figure 7.2 shows that the biggest impact to efficiency is seen in the early stage of growth.

That means that everybody benefits from outreach volume, not just the big laboratories. In fact, the very large laboratories may not benefit from scale; perhaps the infrastructure costs of securing far-flung business has become so high as to be a diseconomy of scale?

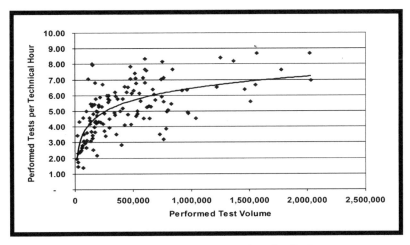

FIGURE 7.2: ECONOMIES OF SCALE FOR PRODUCTIVITY

The same concept of economies of scale can hurt you if you elect to get out of the outreach business. There is a material impact on unit costs. Last year, we performed a strategic options analysis for a three-hospital system on the West Coast. They had a $42 million business and wanted advice on whether they should grow, maintain their base, or exit the business. It turned out that there was a substantial growth opportunity, and they were leaning towards that option. They did not need the cash from a sale. What cemented the decision was the realization that they would incur a 52 percent increase in unit cost for inpatients and outpatients without the outreach volume. Outreach comprised more than half of the laboratory volume and provided tangible economies of scale as well.

CONTRACTING

The national laboratories would like you to believe that they have the advantage when it comes to managed care contracting—that they alone have negotiated "national exclusive contracts" with certain payers that require physician offices to send all patient insurance types to their laboratories. This is hogwash. Or perhaps brainwash is more apropos. They have brainwashed physicians and their office staff that they are required contractually to follow these "rules." Of course, no one wants the inconvenience of using multiple laboratories, so they might as well send all their work to the national laboratory, effectively cutting out the hospital laboratory altogether. Slick? That is their story and they stick with it.

Now, here's the real story. The nationals have negotiated highly discounted, exclusive agreements with certain payers (such as LabCorp for United Healthcare and Quest for Aetna) that rule out other independent laboratories, *but not hospitals*. It's the last part that is conveniently left unsaid. This is one of the best kept secrets of the laboratory industry. The strategy of the national laboratory is to use the exclusive contract to capture what is commonly referred to as "pull-through" business (other insurances and governmental payers, in order to offset losses due to highly discounted fees. The real story is that as long as a hospital has a contract for inpatient services, the laboratory can provide outreach laboratory services. Has anyone ever told you that before? Of course not! It is not in the interest of the national laboratory or the payer. The contracted laboratory is penalized for "leakage," and the profitability of the insurance company goes down because hospitals are reimbursed at a higher rate. Both are incentivized financially to exclude hospital laboratories. Undoubtedly, you will see all manner of marketing materials for physicians and patients to attempt to maintain this untruth.

> ▶ One of the best kept secrets in the laboratory industry is that as long as a hospital has a contract for inpatient services, the laboratory can provide outreach laboratory services—regardless of agreements negotiated by national providers.

So how do you overcome this barrier? Your managed care contractor can have a candid conversation with the insurance company. I have seen many variations of deals that have been forged with insurance companies. In one case, the hospital agreed to accept the independent laboratory fee schedule with an agreement to offset the loss in other parts of the contract. In other cases, hospitals have agreed to accept the same reimbursement as the national laboratory without the offset so that they could garner all the pull-through business. Of course, there are many scenarios in between these two extremes. Each case must be looked at individually because the rates vary widely. Some may make good business sense, others not.

▶ The issue is not *exclusivity*, it is *reimbursement*. Payers have to maintain their contracts with hospitals for inpatient and outpatient services, and that gives you more clout than you realize. Leverage that relationship to benefit the laboratory business.

The issue is not *exclusivity*, it is *reimbursement*. I will talk more about the challenges of pricing and reimbursement in the next section. Suffice it to say that hospitals and health systems have leverage in these conversations. The payers have to maintain their contracts with hospitals for inpatient and outpatient services, and that gives you more clout than you realize. Leverage that relationship to benefit the laboratory business.

PRICING

It is common knowledge that hospitals have higher reimbursement rates compared to commercial laboratories. This gives hospitals a distinct advantage on the revenue side, provided that their pricing is not egregious. Recent movement towards pricing transparency is making it more and more difficult for hospitals to justify or sustain this advantage. After all, there is no real rationale for an outpatient test performed by a hospital laboratory to cost more than a similar outpatient or nonpatient test performed by a commercial laboratory. The rationale only applies to inpatient testing, which has to be done quickly on a 24/7 basis versus being batched once per 24 hours. There *is* a much higher cost for inpatient testing.

For years, pricing has been one of the top five obstacles for laboratory outreach programs nationally (as measured annually in Chi's *Comprehensive National Laboratory Outreach Survey*). In 2014, it became the hottest issue. There are four primary reasons behind this:

- There is a push for greater pricing transparency for all types of health care pricing.
- The Affordable Care Act is driving prices lower.
- More costs are being shifted to patients in the form of higher deductibles and co-pays.
- National laboratories are using fees as a major differentiator from hospitals.

A recent article in the *Wall Street Journal* addressed how pricing transparency emphasizes vast differences in pricing within and across markets. This will most likely drive competition based on cost—something that is new to health care. According to the article, "doctors and hospitals have rarely competed on cost. Third-party payers still foot the bulk of the bills, and many players in the health-care industry benefit from keeping their costs and profit margins murky."[1]

There is another trend afoot in health care that places pricing under the microscope. Employers are asking employees to share the burden of the rising cost of health care insurance. This cost shift comes in the form of increased employee premiums, individual and family deductibles, physician office co-pay amounts, and co-insurance, all of which raise out-of-pocket expenses for individuals. According to the *Wall Street Journal*, the number of patients with deductibles of $1,000 or more rose from 10 percent in 2006 to 38 percent last year. The Affordable Care Act applies family deductibles of $6,000 and $10,000 for Silver and Bronze plans, respectively.[2]

Table 7.1 demonstrates how the higher prices charged by hospitals become a deterrent for patients to use their local hospital rather than Quest, LabCorp, or a regional independent laboratory. The table illustrates that the disincentive involves both a pricing disincentive (i.e., the hospital charge is almost double the average commercial laboratory charge) and a reimbursement premium that is often paid to the hospital-based laboratory providers. This premium comes in the form of increased health care costs for individuals.

The current gap between hospital and independent laboratory reimbursement may be short-lived. At some point in the future, all outpatient and nonpatient laboratory work may be reimbursed under one fee schedule. Some hospitals recognize this and are trying to decide whether to ride the wave for as long as they can under the provider reimbursement model, or adopt the lower independent laboratory fee schedule to be more competitive. While they recognize that their patients are unhappy, they choose to maximize revenues in the short run or exit the business and get maximum value for it. Others have chosen to adopt the independent laboratory fee schedule as a defensive move to prevent a loss of business. Real entrepreneurs have adopted independent laboratory fees to continue to grow and capture new market share. The following two case studies show how this is a highly individualized decision.

TABLE 7.1: IMPACT OF HOSPITAL PRICING ON PATIENTS

	Average Hospital Charge*	Medicare Allowable	Hospital Lab Reimbursement from Managed Care Payer**	Average Commercial Lab Charge***	Commercial Lab Reimbursement from Managed Care Payer****
Total Lab Test Charges	$234	$39	$105	$137	$36
Patient Out-of-Pocket Expense • 20% Co-Insurance • $1,000 Deductible (Not Met)			$105		$36
Patient Out-of-Pocket Expense • 20% Co-Insurance • Deductible (N/A or Met)			$21		$7
Patient Disincentive			3 times higher		-

Note: All dollar amounts have been rounded to the nearest dollar.

*Average hospital charge is approximately six times Medicare and assumes three routine laboratory tests, including phlebotomy.

**Average hospital reimbursement is estimated at 45 percent of hospital charge.

***Average commercial laboratory charge is approximately 3.5 times Medicare.

****Average commercial laboratory reimbursement is estimated at 90 percent of the current Medicare allowable.

Case Study 1: Growth View

A hospital-based outreach program in the western U.S. had grown its program to over $40 million in annual revenues using hospital-based pricing and reimbursement rates. Over the past three years, however, revenue was flat or declining due to patient criticism of the hospital-based pricing structure and the underlying increase in out–of–pocket costs. Executive leadership determined that a strategy to normalize prices, coupled with an aggressive sales growth strategy and managed care negotiation, would best position the organization for the future.

This was a gutsy move. It would take four years to return to current profitability but, taking a longer view, there would be a cumulative operating income of $126 million over ten years and a 30 percent reduction in costs. (See Figure 7.3.) Isn't this what all hospitals are searching for today?

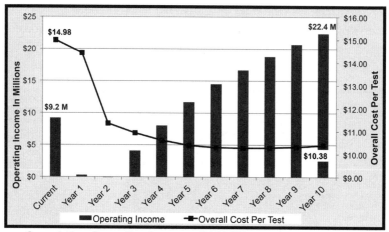

- **Cumulative Operating Income: $126.3M over ten years**
- **30% reduction in unit costs over ten years**

FIGURE 7.3: CASE STUDY—CONVERSION TO INDEPENDENT LABORATORY FEE SCHEDULE

Case Study 2: Status Quo View

A hospital in the northeastern U.S. had grown its outreach program to approximately $9 million in annual revenues using hospital-based pricing. In addition to the outreach division, the organization had a large number of regional outpatient centers offering a variety of patient-centric services, including laboratory services. In this instance, patient criticism of pricing had not been an overriding issue, in part due to the large percentage of outpatient-based laboratory services provided inside the walls of the hospital or hospital-sponsored outpatient sites located strategically throughout the community. The assumption is that patients are more likely to find hospital pricing more palatable in a hospital-specified location.

Executive leadership was interested in a growth strategy to capture a larger percentage of physician office business. After careful consideration of the financial impact, leadership feared that if they lowered fees for outreach, payers might apply the same fees to outpatient services. The reimbursement impact would be untenable. A decision was made by hospital executives to maintain the status quo and ride the wave of reimbursement premiums. The driver was the perceived potential loss of

$123 million in revenue over 10 years. To our knowledge, there has never been an instance where the outreach fee schedule was applied to outpatients. While we thought this outcome was unlikely, we could not say so with certainty. Being risk-adverse, this hospital chose to take the conservative route.

These are examples of two highly personalized strategies for outreach growth and sustaining cash flow. Each organization looks at the situation differently, and decisions are highly influenced by an appetite for growth and the tolerance of risk. One hospital took a higher risk/higher reward approach, while the other played it conservatively. There is never only one right answer.

Depending on your goals, you may have to adjust your pricing. If you want to become a regional laboratory and compete head-to-head with the nationals in an open marketplace, then adopting the independent laboratory fee schedule may be required. If you want to develop a modest business from physicians who are employed or affiliated with your organization (what we call "inreach"), then you may be able to maintain a modest pricing advantage over the nationals. For years, I have predicted that this difference will disappear and reimbursement for all outpatient/nonpatient testing will be standardized. Surprisingly, this has not happened as of this writing, but you would do well to plan for it in your financial models.

REIMBURSEMENT

Hospitals have a distinct reimbursement advantage over independent laboratories. This is based on the higher cost to provide around-the-clock services: seven days per week for hospital patients. In contrast, independent laboratories operate on one shift five days per week, a 21/5 work ratio for hospital versus independent laboratories. Our 2014 *Comprehensive National Laboratory Outreach Survey* found the average and median reimbursement to be $16.87 and $19.51, respectively, for hospitals. Using an average of 3.5 tests per requisition or patient encounter, the average and median reimbursement per requisition is $59.05 and $68.29, respectively. Comparing these hospital rates with $44.00 per requisition for independent laboratories shows a 34 to 55 percent higher reimbursement for hospitals. This represents a huge advantage for hospitals.

BILLING

After IT, billing is the second biggest challenge of outreach programs. Laboratory billing is the most complex, regulated, and risk-prone of all medical billing. Laboratory claims are also often perceived as a nuisance since they are small-dollar compared to other hospital bills (think inpatient stays, surgery, sophisticated diagnostic testing, and interventional treatments). The average laboratory claim of $45 is often less than the write-off amount for hospital bills! It is not uncommon for us to encounter hospital billing departments that do not follow up on laboratory denials. Here are some facts from the 2014 *Comprehensive National Laboratory Outreach Survey* to substantiate these statements:

- 66 percent of outreach programs do not know their bad debt rate.
- 77 percent do not know their days sales outstanding (DSO).
- Only 23 percent are confident that they are collecting everything they can.

Every single day, hospital billing departments leave money on the table that is critical for a business, based on a large volume of small-dollar claims. For this reason, it is strongly recommended that outreach billing be outsourced to a company that specializes in laboratory billing. One note of caution: do not confuse outsourcing with abdication. You can have laboratory billing experts perform the billing *for you*, but you still have to manage their performance.

 One note of caution: do not confuse outsourcing with abdication. Have laboratory billing experts perform the billing *for you*, while you still manage their performance.

Beware of skimming from less-than-stellar companies. They submit claims and take the easy money without following up on denials or chasing down claims with incomplete or inaccurate information. That's your problem. Your responsibility is to submit "clean" (complete and accurate) claims. The billing company sends out the bills and collects the money. A good specialty (laboratory) billing company will provide upside in collections merely by chasing down bills of a much smaller balance than a hospital billing department (down to the $3 to $5 range).

The one caveat is that the billing company must be good, and you have to manage performance. You can't be profitable if you pay seven percent of collections on average to outsource billing, and have unworked denials and aged accounts receivable. This results in a triple whammy: lower than expected collection rates, subsequent write-downs, and lower profitability. I know this seems like common sense, but remember the quote from Horace Greeley: "Common sense is very uncommon." Based on my experience, this definitely applies to billing.

There are two additional advantages to outsourcing billing: it is a great way to segregate outreach revenues from hospital business, and it allows you to determine a specific collection rate for laboratory. Most payments are bundled. Laboratory may be paid as part of a bill covering other hospital services. It is possible to do line-item posting of payments, but very few hospital billing departments take this cumbersome step. As a result, collection rates are an aggregated rate for the hospital overall and may not accurately reflect laboratory collections. Segregation of revenues and knowledge of actual collection rates are key building blocks for the profit and loss statement (P&L), which is the next section of this chapter. Should you be interested in further discussions and detail about billing, please reference our company website (www.chisolutionsinc.com) for articles, industry presentations, and blogs on this subject.

PROFITABILITY

The reimbursement advantage of hospitals transfers to the bottom line. In our 2014 survey, pre-tax operating margin for independent laboratories was 11 percent, compared with a contribution margin for hospital outreach of 28 percent. The largest of the nationals, Quest Diagnostics and LabCorp, had higher margins than independent laboratories as a group (18.9 percent for Quest[3] and 15.8 percent for LabCorp[4]) but still well below hospital laboratory performance.

When we look at subsets of hospital-based businesses, we find that the contribution margin can range as high as 50 percent. What other service business do you know that sports this kind of margin? Typically, system core laboratories outperform stand-alone hospital laboratories. We have not seen any slippage in operating margin over the past few years, despite declining reimbursement. We believe this to be due to the simultaneous focus on cost reductions.

FINANCIAL TRANSPARENCY

All businesses require a profit and loss statement (P&L) to determine profitability. Yet, according to our research, only 41 percent of outreach programs are provided with periodic profitability reports. More than half are not. Forty-six percent do not get reports, and the remaining 14 percent are uncertain. There is an astounding lack of transparency for this business line, which supports earlier assertions that outreach is generally misunderstood. Seriously, how can anyone run a business without a P&L? Why would any hospital allow that in this day and age? Just to put this into context, we are talking about a median and average business of $11 million and $19 million, respectively. These are substantial businesses that are run like a mom-and-pop or, perhaps more appropriately, worse than a mom-and-pop. At least the local family business knows whether they are making money! This is a case of the not-for-profit mentality gone haywire, or alternatively, a view into the surprisingly unsophisticated financial management of hospital business lines.

> ▶ Substantial businesses are run like a mom-and-pop or, perhaps more appropriately, worse than a mom-and-pop. At least the local family business knows whether they are making money!

Everyone knows how to construct a P&L, but not everyone knows what costs to include and exclude. The most common problem we encounter with P&Ls is the misallocation of costs. Misallocation inadvertently makes the outreach program look like a loser. Our philosophy is that the P&L should only contain costs that are specific to outreach: costs that would go away if you decided to exit the business. Therefore, hospital and laboratory overhead should be *excluded*; those costs would *not* go away if you got out of the business. Likewise, facility costs and laboratory equipment are required to support hospital patients. There are specific, unique outreach costs that are appropriate to include, such as courier vehicles, patient service centers, physician connectivity software, interface costs, and new labor costs (outreach manager, phlebotomists, couriers, client services, sales staff, extra specimen processing FTEs, and incremental technical FTEs in labor intensive disciplines like microbiology or cytology).

This past year, a client with a $12 million outreach program contacted us because the profitability of its program was diminishing, and it was reluctant to make a required upgrade to its IT connectivity if the business was not sustainable. The client wanted to know whether to invest in the business for future growth or to exit. We looked at their P&L as a combined hospital/outreach entity, shown in Table 7.2 under "Total." The operating margin was a paltry 2 percent—one-tenth of the expected margin.

> ▶ Our analysis represented a major turnaround in thinking. Outreach was truly accretive; the new revenues helped cover fixed overhead costs and provide $2.3 million in incremental operating margin. Seeing this, the same executives who originally questioned the IT investment now want to accelerate growth.

Next, we analyzed cost allocations between the hospital and outreach and developed separate pro forma for each. Not surprisingly, the outreach program was profitable at 19 percent (very close to the expected range of 20 percent for an independent laboratory billing on the commercial laboratory fee schedule). It was actually the hospital laboratory that was unprofitable at a 19 percent negative operating margin. This makes much more sense, since the hospital has a required investment in laboratory facilities, equipment, and staffing for a 24/7 operation to support the acute, inpatient business. These costs should not be viewed as part of the outreach business, since they would remain even if the hospital decided to exit the business.

Our analysis represented a major turnaround in thinking. Outreach was truly accretive; the new revenues helped cover fixed overhead costs and provide $2.3 million in new operating margin that would be foregone otherwise. Seeing it in this new light, the same executives who originally questioned the IT investment now want to accelerate growth. We also solved a common conundrum for the laboratory. They did not have a competitive IT offering. Growth stagnated. The laboratory asked for capital to upgrade IT which, in turn, was not approved because the laboratory wasn't growing and was viewed as a low margin business—a veritable catch-22 for the laboratory.

TABLE 7.2: P&L

in 000's	Total	Hospital	Outreach
Revenue:			
Inpatient	9,317	$9,317	
Outreach	32,371		32,371
Total Gross Charges	41,688	9,371	32,371
Contractual Adjustments	(20,021)		(20,021)
Bad Debt	(396)		(396)
Net Patient Revenue	21,271	9,317	11,953
Other Operating Revenue	153	99	54
Total Operating Revenue	21,424	9,417	12,007
Expenses:			
Salary and Benefits	9,568	5,510	4,057
Professional Fees and Purchased Services	4,353	2,289	2,064
Internal Assessment	887	396	491
Medical Supplies	4,079	2,327	1,752
Depreciation and Amortization	137	61	76
Other	1,906	640	1,266
Total Expenses	20,930	11,223	9,707
Operating Income	$494	$(1,806)	$2,300
Operating Income %	2.3%	-19.2%	19.2%
Key Statistics			
Test Volume	1,574	671	903
Net Revenue per Test	$13.61	$14.03	$13.30
Total Cost per Test	$13.30	$16.72	$10.75
Salary and Benefit Cost per Test	$6.08	$8.21	$4.49
Supply Cost per Test	$2.59	$3.47	$1.94

I would be remiss if I did not point out another important advantage of outreach: lowering unit costs overall. The blended cost per test of $13.30 distorts the picture. The cost per test for hospital patients is actually 23 percent higher than outreach ($16.72 versus $10.75 for hospital and outreach, respectively). In a similar study conducted two years ago, we estimated that the cost of testing would increase by 30 percent if the system monetized a $42 million outreach program. There are important, unintended consequences of exiting an established business that are not always readily apparent nor appreciated. With volume decreases, the test menu would be pared down and turnaround time would suffer.

PERFORMANCE MANAGEMENT

Management of outreach financial performance is based on the same principles for all businesses: maximizing revenue, and minimizing costs. The three biggest opportunities for maximizing revenue in order of priority are:

- Reimbursement as a hospital or independent laboratory.
- Sales performance.
- Billing efficiency.

There are six ways that you can reduce the amount of money left on the table by billing inefficiencies or just bad business practices. In order of priority, they are:

- **Maximize the use of online order entry systems on the front end (to eliminate errors such as missing or incorrect information).** The most successful laboratories use online order entry for 80 to 90 percent of their client base.

- **Ensure that your billing service is working all denials.** A laboratory with 1,000 patients per day can have a denial rate as high as 30 percent. Not working those claims has a material impact ($5.3 million annually).

- **Confirm that the laboratory follows through on missing billing information within 24 to 48 hours.** Collections are disproportionate to the length of time to follow up, and it is possible to miss filing limits (as little as 90 days for most commercial payers).

- **Use a low write-off balance for laboratory in the \$3 to \$5 range.** This is tenfold less than the typical write-off balance for general hospital services.

- **Do not take "cast off" business from the national laboratories!** If they dumped a client, it is likely because they were not profitable or too high maintenance.

- **Don't be afraid to fire "bad" clients.** All business is not good business. Do not confuse volume with profitability. A client profitability analysis of a Midwestern outreach program revealed that eight of its highest volume clients were not profitable.

From a cost perspective, there are six things that you need to execute to drive down costs:

- Standardize equipment and reagents.
- Maximize synergies from consolidation.
- Grow your outreach program.
- Manage reference lab and blood costs.
- Apply lean practices.
- Participate in a benchmarking service.

Although it is beyond the scope of this book to go into detail on each of these cost reduction strategies, you can find a multitude of information on these topics on our website www.chisolutionsinc.com.

▶ With each iteration of revenue and cost reduction steps, there are new learnings, new technology, and new synergies to improve net revenue and net profits. It is a continuous improvement process.

Suffice it to say that you go through each of these revenue and cost reduction steps and then do them all over again and again. With each iteration, there are new learnings, new technology, and new synergies to improve net revenue and net profits. It is a continuous improvement process.

RISK

The last consideration is risk. Reasonable folks would agree that most hospitals in today's environment, especially the not-for-profits, are risk adverse. So what is the downside of making a mistake? Of failing to execute? Of disappointing results? Not much. Honestly!

It's because the vast majority of investment for outreach is in operating expenses. The capital costs are very modest. The five-year capital requirements are shown in the table below for a range of program sizes: $10 million, $25 million, and $50 million. The first-year capital ranges from $397,000 to $1.0 million and includes the cost of IT connectivity, computers, interfaces, courier vehicles, and upgrading and/or outfitting patient service centers.

TABLE 7.3: OUTREACH PROGRAM–CAPITAL REQUIREMENTS OVER 5 YEARS

	Program Size – $10 Million	Program Size – $25 Million	Program Size – $50 Million
Physician Connectivity plus Interfaces	$882,000	$1,829,000	$3,407,000
Computer Equipment/Printers	55,000	137,000	274,000
Courier Vehicles	137,000	332,000	683,000
Patient Service Center Renovations	90,000	210,000	420,000
Total	$1,163,000	$2,507,000	$4,784,000
Number of Patient Service Centers	6	14	28
Year 1 Estimated Capital Needs	$397,000	$648,000	$1,046,000

Most of the cost of outreach is labor (additional FTEs for the unique outreach infrastructure). Table 7.4 shows a five-year estimate of FTEs required for the same size businesses as above. The range is from 45 to 179 FTEs as shown in the table by job title and in total.

Should business conditions or strategic priorities change at some point in the future, the business can be monetized for roughly 1.0 to 1.5 times revenue. The multiple can be higher for specialty laboratories, but this number is typical of what we have seen in the industry over the last three to five years. And there are always willing buyers—both Quest Diagnostics and LabCorp have grown mostly by acquisition over the last few years.

TABLE 7.4: OUTREACH PROGRAM FTES

Full-Time Equivalents	Program Size		
	$10 Million	$25 Million	$50 Million
Technologist	4.0	10.0	10.0
Non-Technical (Specimen Accessioning/Customer Service)	5.0	12.0	23.0
Phlebotomist	18.0	43.0	86.0
Courier	8.0	18.0	36.0
Information Technology Analyst	3.0	4.0	5.0
Vice President	1.0	1.0	1.0
Outreach Program Manager	1.0	1.0	1.0
Marketing Manager	1.0	1.0	1.0
Sales Representatives	2.0	5.0	10.0
Field Service Representatives	1.0	3.0	5.0
Finance Manager	1.0	1.0	1.0
Total FTEs	**45.0**	**99.0**	**179.0**

The last step in exiting the business would be to right-size staffing for reduced volume and eliminate outreach-specific FTEs (sales, couriers, phlebotomists, specimen processors, billing, and client services). No doubt, reductions in force are emotionally challenging but fairly straightforward from a management perspective. In this context, I view the risk associated with an outreach strategy as low. With a thoughtful analysis of options and good execution, it is easy to exit the business. The ability to monetize without timing constraints further supports a low-risk strategy. Does that surprise you? I think it would surprise many executives who view outreach as difficult, complex, and risky.

CHAPTER SUMMARY

The local outreach program does not have the scale, sophistication, or structure of the national or large regional laboratories. The local mom-and-pop outreach business offers better service. It offers quality products at a fair price. The local outreach program keeps jobs in the community. Most impressive of all, despite the smaller scale of operations, profitability is higher than that of the large, national laboratories.

Key learnings from this chapter are:

· Additional volume from outreach drives down unit costs and improves productivity.

· Access to managed care contracts is not as difficult as perceived if the hospital's relationship to the insurance company is leveraged.

· Depending on the desired size of your business, you may have to adjust your pricing to be competitive with the national and regional laboratories.

· Outsourcing billing to a laboratory-specific expert generally provides the best collection rates and segregates outreach from hospital revenue.

· Profitability of hospital-based programs ranges from 20 to 50 percent of operating margin, far in excess of commercial laboratories.

· Performance management is an ongoing process, both from a cost and a revenue perspective. There is opportunity for every laboratory to improve.

· The business risk of outreach is low due to very modest upfront capital costs. It is easy to exit if the business conditions or strategic priorities change.

There is no doubt that outreach is a viable financial strategy provided you have a willingness to be flexible with contracting, pricing, and billing. Operating margins are high at up to 50 percent with an average of 30 percent. When maximized, outreach can comprise up to 50% of hospital EBITDA from only 5% of the costs. And the risk is low—you can exit and monetize the business at any time to provide needed capital for your hospital or system.

CHAPTER 8

STRUCTURAL REQUIREMENTS

The structure is the foundation upon which the business is built. It determines scale, operating cost, and profitability. Ideally, outreach is set up as a separate company or as a distinct accounting entity to track business performance.

In addition to structure, outreach requires:

- Updated systems (information technology)
- Three- to five-year business plan
- Capital budget
- Operating budget
- P&L developed by Finance
- Management reports

The ideal structure for outreach requires "out of the box" thinking. No doubt many of you have seen the familiar nine-dot puzzle. Try to connect the nine dots with four lines and without raising your pen from the paper:

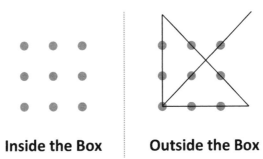

Inside the Box   **Outside the Box**

The puzzle cannot be solved if we limit the lines to the confines of the box. We are forced to think outside the box to solve the puzzle. Wouldn't it be great if all our problems were the same? We would be less likely to settle for obvious and easy but poor choices. Looking at the current state of outreach programs today, the majority are missing key structural and functional requirements, as shown in the comparison of current and future states in Figure 8.1. Most programs today are constrained by "inside the box" thinking.

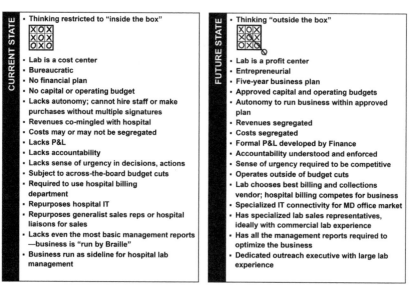

CURRENT STATE

- Thinking restricted to "inside the box"
- Lab is a cost center
- Bureaucratic
- No financial plan
- No capital or operating budget
- Lacks autonomy; cannot hire staff or make purchases without multiple signatures
- Revenues co-mingled with hospital
- Costs may or may not be segregated
- Lacks P&L
- Lacks accountability
- Lacks sense of urgency in decisions, actions
- Subject to across-the-board budget cuts
- Required to use hospital billing department
- Repurposes hospital IT
- Repurposes generalist sales reps or hospital liaisons for sales
- Lacks even the most basic management reports —business is "run by Braille"
- Business run as sideline for hospital lab management

FUTURE STATE

- Thinking "outside the box"
- Lab is a profit center
- Entrepreneurial
- Five-year business plan
- Approved capital and operating budgets
- Autonomy to run business within approved plan
- Revenues segregated
- Costs segregated
- Formal P&L developed by Finance
- Accountability understood and enforced
- Sense of urgency required to be competitive
- Operates outside of budget cuts
- Lab chooses best billing and collections vendor; hospital billing competes for business
- Specialized IT connectivity for MD office market
- Has specialized lab sales representatives, ideally with commercial lab experience
- Has all the management reports required to optimize the business
- Dedicated outreach executive with large lab experience

FIGURE 8.1: OUTREACH PROGRAM CURRENT VS. FUTURE STATE

The contrast between current and future states is startling, yet none of these desired future state characteristics would be considered odd in any other business. Why do they seem so draconian for a business embedded within a hospital?

▶ The contrast between current and future states is startling, yet none of these desired future state characteristics would be considered odd in any other business. Why do they seem so draconian here?

The answer to this question is found in more detail in Chapters 2 and 6. Suffice it to say that most outreach programs today do not function like businesses because the parent organization (not-for-profit) hospitals still do not function like businesses. How else can we explain the tenfold difference in profitability between not-for-profit and for-profit hospitals?

HIGH-LEVEL STRUCTURAL OPTIONS

Let's look at three approaches to structure.

Option 1. Develop a New, Separate Company

This option provides the most flexibility for a scalable business. It has the added advantage of a separate provider number for clean segregation of revenues and costs. It is a little more work and cost upfront, but pays off if you want to develop a large business. It is the most visible and transparent of all the options and the best option for future exit, sale, or merger. This structure would be appropriate for outreach programs in excess of $50 million.

Option 2. Develop a New, Separate Accounting Entity

This option has almost all the benefits of the separate company with less work and cost. The only disadvantage is that reimbursements will be commingled with hospital payments and may not be segregated to the same extent as a separate provider number. This option is adequate for the majority of outreach businesses today.

Option 3. Operate the Business as a Cost Center

This is the standard today. It is woefully inadequate if you want to run a serious business. We do not recommend this option.

Would it be worth it to you to set up the first or second structural option for a $20 million business? Remember, that is just the average. If you're serious about developing this business, it could easily be a multiple of $20 million.

MANAGEMENT AND OPERATIONAL STRUCTURE

What other structural considerations should be taken into account? Management structure is the next priority.

It is beyond foolish to have a $20 million plus business with a 35 percent operating margin run by a part-time middle manager with no autonomy. First, this business needs an experienced CEO who has run businesses of greater size and complexity. Second, the laboratory CEO should report into the parent organization at a very high level (system COO, CFO, or CEO) to ensure maximum success. Third, this executive should have authority over outreach and hospital laboratory operations, because many of the service requirements (quality, test menu, turnaround time, etc.) are run from the hospital side of the laboratory. Lastly, the laboratory CEO should have two full-time direct reports: one over outreach and the other over hospital operations.

> ▶ It is beyond foolish to have a $20 million plus business with a 35 percent operating margin run by a part-time middle manager with no autonomy in a non-profit organization.

Another key decision relates to operational structure. The operational structure must have a competitive expense structure. A study of large outreach programs conducted by Chi in 2015 found that of programs averaging $65 million in net revenue, 75 percent were located in a hospital, versus 25 percent which had offsite, standalone laboratories. Twenty years ago, there was a trend towards building offsite core laboratories to house consolidated system laboratory operations and an autonomous outreach program. The savings from consolidation compared to standalone laboratories was considerable, in the range of 20 to 30 percent. That, combined with outreach, was often sufficient to capitalize a $10 million or more investment in an offsite laboratory.

This strategy is rarely financially viable today, as a result of increased efficiencies of individual laboratories over time. In fact, for the first time ever, hospital-based laboratories were found to have a higher (35 percent) contribution margin than offsite laboratories (30 percent) in our most recent *Fourteenth Comprehensive National Laboratory Outreach Survey*. Time will tell if this trend is sustained or merely a one-year aberration.

FOR-PROFIT VS. NOT-FOR-PROFIT?

Another structural question that comes up is, should the business be for-profit or not-for-profit?

In our experience, this is an individual organizational decision—a distinction that has no meaningful difference on outcomes. Your tax accountants can provide guidance on how to treat the unrelated business income (UBI) of outreach. The key is to make outreach a separate business entity, regardless of whether it is for-profit or not-for-profit.

It may be possible to avoid paying taxes on UBI. Years ago, I was able to set up a not-for-profit laboratory company in the Northeast with an IRS ruling that all revenues were non-taxable because of the benefit to the community. This may still be possible today if the laboratory provides a continuum of care across the whole spectrum (hospital, physician office, extended care, and medical home). All this new revenue and no taxes—wow!

PARTNERSHIP MODELS

The last structural question is the type of joint ventures or partnerships available with outside entities. What are the pros and cons versus going solo? Let's start with the most formal, a joint venture, and work our way down to management agreements.

Based on my personal experience, I estimate that there are less than 20 formal laboratory/hospital joint ventures today. The laboratory companies that enter joint ventures are very large regional (PAML), national (LabCorp, Quest Diagnostics), or international firms (Sonic). Does that surprise you? Many executives have been led to believe that this number is much larger.

Joint ventures are the most formal of all relationships, set up as separate LLCs. Typically long-term, these relationships can span up to 30 years. The managing partner is selected based on equity contribution to the business, whether as capital or a book of business. The large laboratory is almost always the managing partner. Profit-sharing is based on equity. There are pros and cons to formal joint ventures, as described in Table 8.1.

TABLE 8.1: PROS AND CONS OF FORMAL JOINT VENTURES

Pros	Cons
▪ Established models ▪ Provision of capital ▪ Experienced management ▪ Leveraging of support infrastructure (IT, billing, couriers)	▪ Potential loss of management control ▪ Revenue sharing ▪ Fee escalations over time ▪ Track record for meeting service needs

In addition, these attributes may be viewed differently as pros or cons by different parties. From a trending standpoint, the vast majority of joint ventures have been in existence for many years. Few new ventures have occurred in the last few years, and there is increasing attrition of current relationships. In the last five years, we have been asked more often to help clients exit such relationships than to enter. The cause for concern is most often fee escalations over time and/or a dissatisfaction with the share of profits.

The second category of partnerships are non-equity, multi-year management agreements where the partner helps the hospital grow the outreach business and reduce operating costs. The term of these agreements is typically in the five-year range with options to renew. The benefit of non-equity partnerships over joint ventures is that the hospital retains all profits and simply pays the partner a management fee for assistance in growing the business. We are aware of six companies that offer such agreements today:

- Accumen
- Chi Solutions
- LabCorp
- Nichols Management Group
- Quest Diagnostics
- United West Labs

There are pros and cons to each offering. Since Chi is one of the companies included, I will provide questions to consider when choosing a partner, rather than make comparisons:

- Understand qualification criteria (such as size of current business, market opportunity, etc.).
- Know the risks and rewards for each party and alignment thereof.
- Determine if fees are fixed or performance-based, and know your preference.
- Ascertain the company's number of other similar agreements and track record in working with other hospitals and systems.
- Identify potential conflict(s) of interest and/or willingness to enter into non-competition agreements in your market.

As you can see, there are a variety of structural options and business models. You may be able to customize your deal to avoid or mitigate the known pitfalls. One thing I know for sure: when you've seen one, you have seen *only* one. No matter what anybody tells you, every one of the companies listed may have their ideal plan, but each has its exceptions. It's up to you to make your deal the best it can be.

> ▶ There are many structural options and business models. When you've seen one, you have seen *only* one. Each company listed may have an ideal plan, but everyone has exceptions. It's up to you to make your deal the best it can be.

In general terms, partnerships offer hospitals something of value, or else there would be no market for these types of services. Most often, the benefits accrue from sales sophistication, the leveraging of existing infrastructure, and access to purchasing agreements or cost reduction strategies. In our experience, overall performance is superior to self-managed programs. As always, the devil is in the details.

Other factors that may lead to specific structural options include planning for future monetization, merger, or rollup. As Stephen Covey used to say, "begin with the end in mind."[1] If you know you are going to grow the business and monetize at some point in the future, plan for a separate entity that can be easily carved out. The same is true for initial public offerings (IPOs), mergers, joint ventures, or rollup strategies. Figure 8.2 illustrates options through the evolution of a business.

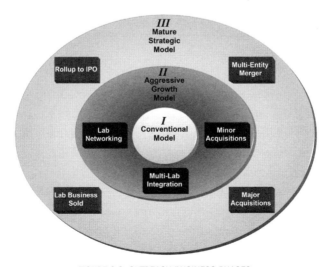

FIGURE 8.2: OUTREACH BUSINESS PHASES

It is desirable to choose the structural options that give the most flexibility and have the best fit with your strategic goals. Even if you don't plan on a big play like IPO, joint venture, or merger, it is still a good business practice to set up a separate accounting entity for potential future monetization. It is much easier to develop a credible P&L and valuation for a separate entity than one that is intermixed with outpatient business.

MANAGEMENT REPORTS

The last critical success factor for outreach is the provision of all the information needed to run the business. You may wonder why I'm taking the time to talk about something so simplistic. It's so basic and simple, it's often overlooked. When asked if they had the information, management reports, and key performance indicators to manage their business, only 28 percent of laboratory directors and executives responded in the affirmative. Nearly three-quarters of executives are forced to manage intuitively, to "feel" their way because they lack actionable management reports. I call this "managing by Braille."

> ▶ Only 28 percent of laboratory directors and executives said they had the information, management reports, and key performance indicators to manage their business. Nearly three-quarters of executives are forced to manage intuitively, to "feel" their way because they lack actionable management reports. I call this "managing by Braille."

Table 8.2 provides examples of the most basic information needed to run a business and the percent of laboratories that have access to this information. While recent Chi surveys show improvement in the number of respondents that possess this data, most laboratories still fall well short with regard to several crucial metrics.

The lack of information to manage hospital-based outreach programs is astounding. What other $19 million, for-profit business would operate like this? Just imagine the potential if management had access to the information it needed to run the business like a real, for-profit company? The untapped potential is material and worth investigating.

TABLE 8.2: MANAGEMENT BY BRAILLE

Metric	% with Access to Info	Metric	% with Access to Info
General Business Metrics		**Customer Service**	
Net (collected) revenue per requisition	67%	# of calls per service rep per day	57%
Profitability overall	77%	Hold time for incoming calls	57%
Profitability by client	25%	Rate of abandoned calls	50%
Performance by sales rep	22%		
Specimen Processing		**Testing**	
Volume of tests	77%	Corrected reports	75%
Specimens with inadequate volume	74%	Quality control failures	64%
Data entry errors	66%	Turnaround time by client	56%
Specimen integrity compromised	60%		
Volume by hour of day	36%		
Billing		**Couriers**	
Bad debt	43%	Ability to track specimens	31%
Days sales outstanding	39%		
Confident collecting everything you can	26%		

Note: Percentage of laboratories with access to information.

CHAPTER SUMMARY

Structure provides the foundation for the business—it determines its ability to operate, to compete, and to scale. Here is the "must have" list:

· Consider the pros and cons of partnerships versus a self-managed model.

· Set up outreach as a separate company or separate accounting entity under the hospital.

· Ensure appropriate financial planning, reporting and accountability.

· Appoint a CEO with experience in running a business of two to three times your current size.

· Provide the necessary autonomy to operate within approved capital and operating budgets without additional approvals.

· Make available all the necessary information and management reports to run the business.

· Get out of the way and let them run like a true business.

CHAPTER 9

SALES

Sales is always among the top five weaknesses reported by hospitals and health systems in our annual *Comprehensive National Laboratory Outreach Survey*.

Why? Because sales is an enigma to hospitals. Sure, hospitals have marketing and communications, but sales? Not really.

Sales is a very different skill set than marketing and is only recently gaining importance as health systems consolidate and compete. The converse is true about the laboratory industry. As noted in Chapter 1, the large national laboratories (Quest Diagnostics and LabCorp) have had experienced, highly skilled, highly trained, and highly compensated "hunters" (sales representatives totally focused on growth) for decades. Most hospital outreach programs have "hybrid" representatives that juggle both sales and service and are not as well-trained, compensated, or productive as their for-profit competitors. The difference in results is staggering, especially when viewed on a cumulative basis.

We will get to that shortly, but first let's start with how the business is built from the ground up. Laboratory is the proverbial goose that laid the golden egg for health systems. Each year the number of eggs gets larger and larger because of the power of a recurring revenue model (from maintaining the base business), combined with the growth of new business. Growth can be exponential because of an industry secret called the rule of 78.

> ▶ Laboratory is the proverbial goose that lays the golden egg for health systems. Each year, the number of eggs gets larger and larger because of the power of a recurring revenue model (from maintaining the base business), combined with the growth of new business.

Here's how it works. Each month, a new account (golden egg) is added. As long as there is no attrition, the business grows by 78 times the value of the account in the first year. The typical physician office client (internal medicine, family practice, or OB/GYN) averages about $5,500 to $6,000 in revenue per month. The total number of cells in the spreadsheet for one year is 78. Therefore, a quick way to calculate annual sales at various revenue targets is to multiply the average revenue per customer by the number of cells in a year ($5,500 x 78 = $429,000 in annual revenue). Refer to the example shown in Table 9.1.

TABLE 9.1: RULE OF 78

Month 1	Month 2	Month 3	Month 4	Month 5	Month 6	Month 7	Month 8	Month 9	Month 10	Month 11	Month 12	TOTAL
5,500	5,500	5,500	5,500	5,500	5,500	5,500	5,500	5,500	5,500	5,500	5,500	66,000
	5,500	5,500	5,500	5,500	5,500	5,500	5,500	5,500	5,500	5,500	5,500	60,500
		5,500	5,500	5,500	5,500	5,500	5,500	5,500	5,500	5,500	5,500	55,000
			5,500	5,500	5,500	5,500	5,500	5,500	5,500	5,500	5,500	49,500
				5,500	5,500	5,500	5,500	5,500	5,500	5,500	5,500	44,000
					5,500	5,500	5,500	5,500	5,500	5,500	5,500	38,500
						5,500	5,500	5,500	5,500	5,500	5,500	33,000
							5,500	5,500	5,500	5,500	5,500	27,500
								5,500	5,500	5,500	5,500	22,000
									5,500	5,500	5,500	16,500
										5,500	5,500	11,000
											5,500	5,500
5,500	11,000	16,500	22,000	27,500	33,000	38,500	44,000	49,500	55,000	60,500	66,000	429,000

The growth compounds over time. The rule for Year 2 is 222 times revenue. For Years 3, 4, and 5, apply the rules of 366, 510, and 654, respectively. Growth builds year-over-year way beyond what would be expected in a normal business. The same numbers as above extrapolate to $3.6 million in Year 5. The longer the term, the more powerful the impact. This is the secret behind the multi-billion revenues of Quest and LabCorp. They are built on decades of year-over-year compounding revenues.

Now that we are beginning to get an appreciation for how revenue grows, let's go back to our example. The rule of 78 example was for one sales representative.

- What if you had multiple sales representatives?

- What if you also had service representatives that maintained and upgraded the base business at half the new revenue rate of a sales representative?
- What if you could attract the best hunters—representatives who could generate (and make) two to three times the revenue of the average representative?

To illustrate this point, let's look at the compounding impact of varying levels of performance over time. Figure 9.1 shows the comparative impact of $2,000 per month up to $8,000 per month in new net revenue.

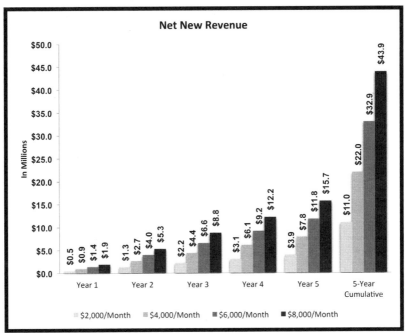

Note: Assumes two sales personnel and two service representatives.

FIGURE 9.1: COMPOUNDING IMPACT OF PERFORMANCE

Now we begin to see how differences in performance can be magnified even further over time, on top of the compounding effect. In the rest of this chapter, we will explore how to build a sales infrastructure based on people, process, and technology to drive exceptional performance for your laboratory.

PEOPLE

PROCESS

TECHNOLOGY

FIGURE 9.2: PEOPLE, PROCESS, AND TECHNOLOGY

PEOPLE

Just like other businesses, it all starts with selecting the right people for the right position and providing the necessary structure and rewards to drive the desired behavior. Key characteristics of successful sales and service representatives are outlined in Table 9.2.

TABLE 9.2: CHARACTERISTICS OF SALES AND SERVICE REPRESENTATIVES

Title	Sales Representatives	Service Representatives
Common Name	Hunter	Farmer
Description	Responsible for finding and selling new business from new customers	Responsible for maintaining the base business and upgrading business within existing customers
Key Traits	<ul><li>Positive attitude</li><li>Congenial</li><li>Self-motivated</li><li>Responsible; proven track record</li><li>Well organized</li><li>Empathic</li><li>Resilient</li><li>Confident</li><li>*Ego-driven*</li><li>*Competitive*</li><li>*Compensation-driven*</li></ul>	<ul><li>Positive attitude</li><li>Congenial</li><li>Self-motivated</li><li>Responsible; proven track record</li><li>Well organized</li><li>Empathic</li><li>Resilient</li><li>Confident</li><li>*Customer-driven*</li><li>*Less competitive*</li><li>*Less compensation-driven*</li></ul>

There are numerous external sources for recruiting salespeople (professional recruiters specializing in laboratory sales, networking, professional organizations, conferences, and advertising). We have 30 years of experience in hiring salespeople, and we use a recruiter. Any number of companies (such as Caliper in Princeton, New Jersey) offer aptitude tests to qualify candidates. We highly recommend using aptitude tests as a first screening tool prior to spending time on the interview process. You will be surprised at the number of candidates that fall out through this process.

Specific job roles (hunter vs. farmer) and compensation systems (salary vs. salary plus incentives) attract different types of salespeople. Generally speaking, in the early years of growth, it's best to start with hunter sales representatives who are competitively compensated to grow the business. Some of the key differences we see between hospital and commercial laboratory sales representatives are:

- Hospital representatives typically have a **smaller percentage of commission versus salary** (35 percent for hospitals versus 56 percent for independent laboratories). In other words, they have a higher base and less incentive. Salespeople who prefer salary are more customer-centered. They like to focus on problem solving and are motivated by security, belonging to a group, and professional development. They want direction from management and have a lower tolerance for risk. They like the security of a guaranteed income and are willing to accept lower pay in exchange. These folks are classified as "farmers." They focus on developing the business through client relationships.

- Most hospital sales representatives are **not given bonuses or higher incentives for exceeding quota**, unlike independent laboratory salespeople. Incentives to exceed quota are common in the independent laboratory world. Well over half of independent laboratories (up to 100 percent, depending upon the specialty) pay incentives for exceeding quota compared to 36 percent of hospital laboratories.

- The last key difference is the **time period to payment of incentives**. Hospital laboratories pay incentives less frequently—quarterly (60 percent), annually (25 percent), and semi-annually (10 percent)—whereas independent laboratories pay monthly (33 percent), quarterly (33 percent), and semi-annually (22 percent). Compensation specialists agree that the reward is more powerful if it is closely tied to the behavior.

▶ Specific job roles (hunter vs. farmer) and compensation systems (salary vs. salary plus incentives) attract different types of salespeople. In the early years of growth, it's best to start with hunter sales representatives who are competitively compensated to grow the business.

It is beyond the scope of this book to do a detailed review on compensation programs for sales. In summary, according to a 2011 Chi survey on laboratory sales and service representative compensation,[1] hospital compensation for sales representatives has not kept up with independent laboratories. In fact, the average compensation at independent laboratories is 34 percent higher than hospitals (total compensation of $126,456 on average for independent laboratories compared to $94,168 for hospitals). The average hospital sales representative has a base of $65,000 and incentives of $30,000 (a 70–30 split between base and commissions). In contrast, the average independent laboratory sales representative has a base of $75,000 and incentives of $52,000 (a 60-40 split of base and commissions).

The most successful salespeople prefer lower ratios of base/commission, some exceeding 50 percent commission. Here's a test to see if you have a hunter or a farmer. Ask your salesperson if she would be willing to lower her base for a higher upside. Use a ratio of 1:2 so that if the base is lowered by $10,000, they have an opportunity to earn $20,000. You have a true hunter if she jumps at this opportunity. She might ask for verification to make sure she understands, but she's in. If you have a farmer, he will opt out, ask you a million questions, say he needs time to think about it, etc. A farmer sees higher risk in lower compensation.

 The most successful salespeople prefer lower ratios of base/commission, some exceeding 50 percent commission.

For service representatives, compensation is comparable as a total and percentage of base and incentives between hospitals and independent laboratories. The average total compensation is $74,267 for hospitals and $75,815 for independent laboratories, with a 64-36 split of base to commissions.[2]

Sales managers are also compensated similarly at hospitals and independent laboratories. The average total compensation at hospitals is $140,356, compared to $141,476 at independent laboratories, with a 60-40 split of base to incentives.[3] Only the largest outreach programs have enough salespeople to require a full-time sales manager. The typical span of control is in the range of six to ten. There are options for part-time sales management from a number of laboratory consulting firms, or you could have a "selling manager," one who has a quota along with management responsibilities. Salespeople are notoriously difficult to manage, and the best salespeople can be the toughest challenge.

> ▶ Do not try DIY sales management if you are not a sales professional. Laboratory directors or executives don't have the experience or the performance management systems to drive maximum sales results.

Do not try DIY sales management if you are not a sales professional! Laboratory directors or executives do not have the experience or the performance management systems to drive maximum sales results. I know this, because I have tried myself and failed when I was running laboratories and have since seen many others follow my path to, at best, mediocre and, at worst, poor results. There is no substitute for management experience. It drives results and, more than any other factor, revenue growth is the key driver of success in this business.

> ▶ There is no substitute for management experience. It drives results. More than any other factor, revenue growth is the key driver of success in this business.

Another key aspect to consider is specialization. The independent laboratory salespeople are, of course, laboratory sales specialists because the companies are laboratory-specific. Our 2014 *Comprehensive National Laboratory Outreach Survey* found that 70 percent of hospital outreach programs use specialists and 30 percent use generalists. When asked about the relative success of the two models, the results were about even (52 percent identifying the multiple service model as less successful, 43 percent about the same, and six percent as more successful).

> ▶ Because of the complexity of laboratory and the long learning curve for this industry, our experience and strong preference is for laboratory salespeople to be specialists.

Our experience is different. Because of the complexity of laboratory and the long learning curve for this industry, our experience and strong preference is for laboratory salespeople to be specialists:

- Laboratory has over 3,500 tests, compared to other service lines which may have only about a dozen.
- Laboratory is comprised of myriad subspecialties (chemistry, hematology, bacteriology, mycology, parasitology, virology, genetics, proteomics, blood bank, etc.).
- Laboratory is a language unto its own.
- Laboratory has the longest learning curve of sales in health care.
- Your competition has specialists and subspecialist salespeople.

Ignore these facts at your peril. A few years ago, we provided outsourced sales support for a three-hospital system in the Midwest for several years under the laboratory specialty model. The hospital had previously decided that it wanted to integrate the laboratory sales team members and make them generalists in an effort to improve their productivity and coordination. The hospital had also taken over management of the sales representatives. Within two years, and as a result of the system's DIY efforts, laboratory revenue dropped by 50 percent. Eventually, the hospital converted back to the specialist model, but it took years to rebuild the business.

There is one combination that makes sense from both a sales and clinical perspective: combining laboratory and imaging in a "diagnostics" sales model. Both specialties are high revenue drivers for health systems. They are becoming more integrated from a clinical standpoint. And studies have shown that one-third of patients who have laboratory testing have concurrent imaging exams. There are some efficiencies to be gained by having one salesperson address both services. There are economies involved with including a laboratory collection site at imaging centers. And best of all, the co-location is good for your patients—one-stop shopping!

Figure 9.3 shows the cycle of recruiting, selecting, training and managing salespeople.

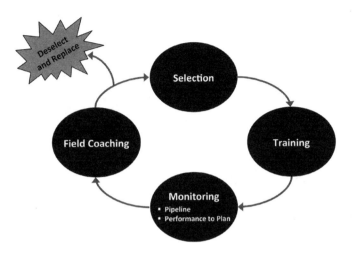

FIGURE 9.3: CYCLE OF RECRUITING, SELECTING, TRAINING, AND MANAGING SALESPEOPLE

Wherever you can, minimize risks and maximize performance through classroom training, tools for performance management, and field coaching. The most common mistakes hospitals make are:

- Inability to recruit high-performing salespeople
- Lack of tools for performance management
- Taking too long to replace a non-performing resource
- Misaligned compensation and sales or strategic plans
- Failure to understand lab-specific compliance regulations

Remember that poor performance for any of the reasons above is magnified over time by the rule of 78. I met a colleague recently who had just fired a long-term sales representative who hadn't sold anything in a year. I was horrified. That is way too long to tolerate poor performance. It may have a material impact on your ability to hit your numbers. Figure 9.4 shows the impact of firing a salesperson after three, six, nine, and twelve months. You sacrifice millions in revenue over a five-year period as a result of the inability to make a tough and timely decision.

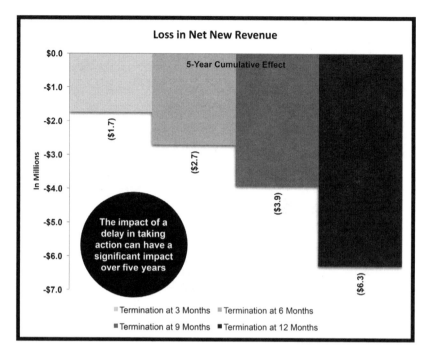

FIGURE 9.4: IMPACT OF SALES REPRESENTATIVE TERMINATION ON NET REVENUE

It is also important to understand compliance training as a risk mitigation strategy in this industry. Compliance training for laboratory sales and service representatives is essential to avoid running afoul of the Stark Law and anti-kickback statutes. The first priority is to be structured and operating in a legal and compliant manner. Running a successful outreach program that operates within those parameters requires expertise. When in doubt, get expert advice.

Training, in general, is a key driver of performance for salespeople. As noted in Figure 9.3, the cycle includes training and retraining as an ongoing, cyclical process. There are two types of training: classroom training and field coaching. The initial classroom training helps the salespeople understand the consultative nature of the sales process. As physicians have merged into larger groups, the sales process has become even more and more complicated. There are a different number of steps, more stakeholders, and an extended process and timeline associated with so called "large account sales." A colleague and friend, Tom Searcy of Hunt Big Sales (www.huntbigsales.com), has extensive training, tools, and support for those who want more depth in this area.

The net result of all the common mistakes listed above is that hospital outreach programs have a wide variability in performance to quota, as demonstrated in Chi's *Fourteenth Comprehensive National Laboratory Outreach Survey*:

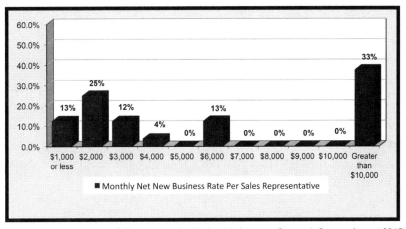

Source: Chi Solutions, 14th Comprehensive National Laboratory Outreach Survey, August 2015.

FIGURE 9.5: PERFORMANCE OF OUTREACH PROGRAM SALES REPRESENTATIVES

The mathematical average is $4,125 per month in new net revenue, yet there are very few average performers. Performance does not resemble a typical bell curve. There are clusters at the low end (poor performers) and high end (good performers) and very few in the middle. It seems as though there is much opportunity to improve sales performance.

PROCESS

A sales plan is the first step from a process point of view and includes the following components:

- Analyze the market.
- Determine a growth target for the coming year.
- Define territories.
- Identify a market segment (e.g., the physician office).

- Identify high laboratory-user physician specialties to target (e.g., internal medicine, family practice, OB/GYN).
- Delineate numbers and types of resources and roles (sales versus service versus hybrid model).
- Identify quotas needed by resource to achieve the revenue target.

The sales plan is not a static plan. It is evolutionary. It evolves with the business and the needs at various stages of the business. It is done minimally on an annual basis. Sometimes it is necessary to revise during the course of the year if there are major disruptions in a market or if performance is behind plan. An experienced manger will know intuitively when to revise a sales plan.

The second step is developing performance management processes, tools, metrics, and reports. The most important are the sales cycle, a pipeline of opportunities, and a tool to forecast sales for the next three months. Each program establishes its own sales cycle with three to five steps. Criteria for each step are defined, and revenue is weighted as a prospect goes through the cycle. For example, Chi's sales cycle is shown in Figure 9.6.

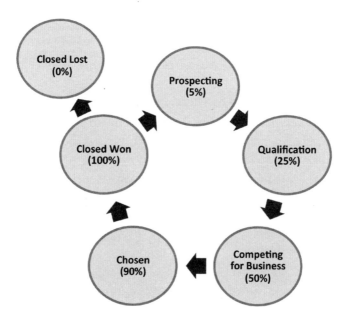

FIGURE 9.6: SALES CYCLE

A revenue forecast is a byproduct of the process, based on expected close dates, the estimated value of the account, and the probability of closing the business. This looks deceptively simple, but is really quite complex. It's more art than science. The challenge is to make it as accurate as possible through adherence to process and vetting by the sales manager. Some examples:

- A sales representative projects modest revenue and is conservative in estimating the date and probability of closing the account. A second salesperson overestimates revenue and the closing date. Which would you rather have? Do you want to be stuck explaining why you didn't hit your numbers month after month, quarter after quarter?

- Another scenario is the salesperson who has a robust pipeline with lots of opportunities but never goes anywhere, getting stuck somewhere in the sales process. Compare this to someone with a modest but realistic pipeline who has the discipline to follow the process. Guaranteed, the latter representative's numbers will be better than the previous.

- Lastly, if you're in a state that allows discounting to physicians, beware of salespeople who appear to have several large, "too good to be true" accounts in their pipeline. If they seem too good to be true, they probably are. Large from a revenue perspective does not equate to profitability. "Large" discount clients can be more work and less profitable than smaller, third-party bill accounts.

A strategic sales plan will protect against commodification of the business. You can limit the amount of client bill or low price business (for example 30 percent of the total) and ensure that your salesforce can sell based on value (70 percent of the business) to protect profitability.

A good sales manager will vet all opportunities to make sure that the business is good business. A good sales manager will help the salesperson figure out why an opportunity is stuck at a certain point in the sales process. A good sales manager will ferret out inaccurate revenue estimates or closing dates. A good sales manager will work with sales representatives in the field, observing their skills and techniques, providing real-time coaching, and helping them close difficult opportunities. A good sales manager can select, develop, and coach teams that will drive sales of one-and-a-half to two times the average. These managers are worth their weight in gold.

TECHNOLOGY

The pipeline and forecast can be as simple as an Excel spreadsheet or as complex as a customer relationship management (CRM) tool. We have used both in our practice. For a small program, the spreadsheet method is more than adequate, but it is not optional—it's in the must-have category.

As the business grows, we recommend investing in a CRM. Advantages include:

- Robust documentation of the history of each client.

- Communication vehicle for sales, service, and management. Everyone can be up-to-date on client issues at a glance.

- Visibility of performance at any time with detail by representative, account, and rollup dashboard.

- User-friendly management reports to track average revenue, close rates, days in the sales cycle, etc., as a group or by individual.

- Segregation of the business by client (physician) bill (if allowed in your state) and third party.

- Segregation of the business by market segment (physician, long-term care, reference laboratory, etc.).

- Documentation of reasons for wins and losses.

- If you have an outsourced billing service and know true collected (verses calculated) revenue by client, you can monitor profitability by client and by salesperson.

- Reports can be further customized by courier route. The most profitable business is added on to an existing courier route.

- The level of sophistication is proportional to the size of the business. Used appropriately, there is a tangible return. At Chi, we use a proprietary version of Salesforce.com that we have customized, based on our sales process and requirements to go from one stage to another in the process. Stage-specific criteria are clearly identified, along with checklists or documentation requirements. This is helpful to both salespeople and management, to track progress over time and understand pipeline projections for the next three months. It also gives operations a sneak preview of potential new clients and estimated volumes.

When would this tool be in the must-have category? Perhaps in the $8-10 million range. It is highly unlikely that a laboratory could grow much beyond this without this level of sophistication. There is a case to install a CRM earlier if the long-range plans are for multiple years of growth. Do you want to be a mom-and-pop operation or a serious business?

CONCLUSION

Let's go back to our analogy of outreach as the goose that laid the golden egg. Our goal is to maximize egg production (new accounts) as well as the size (dollar value) and color (physician specialty that orders high amounts of laboratory testing) of accounts as shown in Figure 9.3. Be mindful of the conditions that make geese (salespeople) happy and you will get the desired outcome.

TABLE 9.3: GOOSE THAT LAID THE GOLDEN EGG VS. OUTREACH

	Goose	Outreach Business
Characteristic	Number of eggs Egg size Egg color	Number of new accounts Revenue Physician specialty
Conditions	Coop versus free range Feed Treats Light, temp, humidity, cleanliness, health maintenance	Structure Base salary Incentive Competitive offering
Outcome	Large numbers of jumbo eggs of the desired color	Large numbers of highly profitable accounts within desired physician specialties

CHAPTER SUMMARY

Laboratory is the proverbial goose that laid the golden egg. Because of the powerful, recurring revenue model (rule of 78), the growth rate is compounded dramatically over time. The secret to maximum growth is your sales model:

· Hiring the appropriate numbers and types of sales resources for your market.

· Training your resources as professional hunters and rewarding them handsomely.

· Developing tools and processes for performance management.

· Replacing substandard resources quickly.

All of your systems, processes, and tools must be fine-tuned to provide the conditions to reach maximum output. Poor performance is magnified over time just like good performance. This shouldn't be a hard choice.

CHAPTER 10

RISK VERSUS REWARD

In this final chapter, I like to close with a candid discussion of risks versus rewards. I will share some of the common mistakes we see in our consulting practice and how to avoid or correct them so that you can maximize the financial impact. Usually these are either design or execution flaws that can be easily rectified once you understand their impact. Secondly, I'll summarize the financial risks versus rewards and show how to evaluate the business risk like a venture capitalist. Last, I will provide other important, non-financial downstream benefits.

FIVE THINGS HOSPITAL EXECUTIVES DO THAT (INADVERTENTLY) KILL OUTREACH

I'd like to help you ward off the most common mistakes made by executives in implementing outreach. There are five top things that hospital executives unwittingly do to make it difficult or impossible for laboratories to succeed at community-based outreach programs:

- Failing to identify outreach as an organizational priority.
- Treating the outreach program like a "cost center."
- Charging hospital prices for community-based work.
- Starving the program for capital.
- Under-resourcing the program.

Surely it is not intentional. Executives do not try to undermine outreach, but that can be the unintended result. Any one of the above constraints can slow growth; together, they result in a material loss of revenue and margin and unhappy physicians and patients. Let's explore each of these constraints to understand why they exist and what can be done to eliminate them.

Failing to Identify Outreach as an Organizational Priority

A successful outreach program requires strong organizational support and alignment around the business. The laboratory depends on many different hospital departments for outreach to flourish: managed care for access to payer contracts, finance for competitive pricing and management reports, billing for maximizing collections, legal for contract review, information technology (IT) for physician office connectivity and interfaces to electronic medical records (EMRs), and human resources for hiring of staff. The whole is only as strong as its weakest link.

FIGURE 10.1: THE CHAIN OF LABORATORY OUTREACH

Treating Outreach Like a "Cost Center"

Most outreach programs are treated like cost centers, rather than revenue-generating business units. They do not have a formal profit and loss statement (P&L) that is vetted by both the laboratory and the finance department. Costs and revenues are embedded in other entities and are not visible or appreciated throughout the organization. Staff is paid at hospital rates, which are not competitive with independent laboratories. The laboratory is benchmarked against others that do not have outreach programs and have very different cost structures. To make matters worse, there is no consideration for the revenue side of the equation. As a result, the business suffers—it cannot function like a true business. Financial results are a fraction of the true potential, the organization loses out on a powerful revenue and margin driver, and naysayers prove that outreach is not profitable. It becomes a self-fulfilling prophecy.

Have you ever considered setting up outreach as a unique accounting entity? Treat it as a separate business unit to easily track performance and provide visibility and accountability for results.

Charging Hospital Prices for Community-Based Work

According to Chi's *Comprehensive National Laboratory Outreach Survey*, hospital pricing is identified as the number one weakness of outreach programs. On average, hospital outpatient charges are 1.5 to 3.0 times that of independent national or regional laboratories. Overcharging for these services results in a disincentive for physicians and patients to use hospital services for what is termed "non-patient" or outreach business. ("Non-patient" refers to specimens that are picked up from doctors' offices and transported to the hospital laboratory for processing.) As a result of higher co-pays and deductibles, patients are increasingly bearing the burden of a higher proportion of health care costs. When it comes to choosing between the local hospital and a national or regional independent laboratory, the cost differential drives behavior. This phenomenon is demonstrated in Table 10.1, which shows out-of-pocket costs for patients using a local hospital.

In this example, the patient pays three times more when using a hospital for community-based work rather than an independent laboratory. Some examples are more extreme. It is easy to see how higher costs at hospitals can drive patients away.

There is no rationale for charging hospital pricing for community-based testing. This type of testing does not require rapid turnaround time or special handling as is often the case with acutely ill patients. Rather, this work is collected and tested in large batches on off-shifts.

TABLE 10.1: PATIENT DISINCENTIVE TO USE HOSPITAL LABORATORY

	Average Hospital Charge*	Medicare Allowable	Hospital Lab Reimbursement from Managed Care Payer**	Average Commercial Lab Charge***	Commercial Lab Reimbursement from Managed Care Payer****
Total Lab Test Charges	$234	$39	$105	$137	$36
Patient Out-of-Pocket Expense ▪ 20% Co-Insurance ▪ $1,000 Deductible (Not Met)			$105		$36
Patient Out-of-Pocket Expense ▪ 20% Co-Insurance ▪ Deductible (N/A or Met)			$21		$7
Patient Disincentive			3 times higher		-

Note: All dollar amounts have been rounded to the nearest dollar.

*Average hospital charge is approximately six times Medicare and assumes three routine laboratory tests, including phlebotomy.

**Average hospital reimbursement is estimated at 45 percent of hospital charge.

***Average commercial laboratory charge is approximately 3.5 times Medicare.

****Average commercial laboratory reimbursement is estimated at 90 percent of the current Medicare allowable.

Commercial payers still reimburse hospitals at higher rates than independent laboratories, but this practice is not sustainable. In the future, non-patient testing will likely be paid on one fee schedule, irrespective of whether the facility is a hospital or independent laboratory. Forward-thinking hospitals are already shifting to the independent laboratory fee schedule in order to mitigate attrition of base business or to jump-start growth. They recognize that they have gone as far as they can go with the old provider-based pricing model.

Why not consider your options to convert to an independent laboratory fee schedule now? You may be able to capture market share, sustain a higher base business, and position your laboratory for the future before non-patient fees are regulated further. This is not for everyone, however; the decision to change to independent laboratory pricing is highly dependent upon the size of the current business.

Starving the Program for Capital

The capital requirements for outreach are modest at approximately $397,000 at inception and an average $192,000 per annum thereafter.

The majority of the costs are technology-related, such as a web-based connectivity solution for physicians to order laboratory tests and receive results, as well as interfaces to the physicians' EMRs or practice management systems. More minor components of capital include the cost of outfitting patient service centers where blood or other specimens are collected for testing. A summary of capital costs for a startup outreach program ($10 million in net revenue by Year 5) is provided in Table 10.2.

TABLE 10.2: STARTUP CAPITAL COSTS

Capital Requirements	Year 1	Year 2	Year 3	Year 4	Year 5	Total
Physician Connectivity Costs	$376,000	$126,000	$126,000	$126,000	$126,000	$882,000
Computer Equipment/ Printers	$5,000	$8,000	$11,000	$14,000	$17,000	$55,000
Courier Vehicles	$0	$39,000	$19,500	$39,000	$39,000	$137,000
Patient Service Center Renovations	$15,000	$30,000	$15,000	$15,000	$15,000	$90,000
Total	$397,000	$203,000	$172,000	$194,000	$197,000	$1,163,000

The rate of return on this modest investment is favorable. Chi has seen large outreach programs that generate incremental operating margin of up to 40 percent and comprise up to 50 percent of hospital EBITDA over time. Progressive organizations view the laboratory as a capital generator rather than a consumer.

Under-Resourcing the Program

The majority of the investment required for outreach is in operating costs, specifically supplementing the technical resources of the laboratory with support staff to collect (phlebotomists), transport (couriers), and process specimens; report results; and bill for services. The two most common problems encountered an inadequate number of staff, and a lack of timeliness in hiring staff. Both are competitive disadvantages in the marketplace.

Very few laboratories have the ability to hire staff based on a pre-approved business plan. The average outreach program brings in $10 million in revenue and has a range of 20-35 full-time equivalents (FTEs), as demonstrated in Table 10.3.

TABLE 10.3: CUMULATIVE INCREMENTAL FTES FOR A $10 MILLION BUSINESS

Incremental FTEs – Cumulative	Year 1	Year 2	Year 3	Year 4	Year 5
Phlebotomists	3.0	8.0	11.0	15.0	18.0
Support Staff (Specimen Accessioning, Customer Service, etc.)	1.0	2.0	3.0	4.0	5.0
Laboratory Technologists	2.0	2.0	3.0	4.0	4.0
Couriers	1.0	3.0	4.0	6.0	8.0
Information Technology	2.0	2.0	3.0	3.0	3.0
Vice President	1.0	1.0	1.0	1.0	1.0
Outreach Manager	1.0	1.0	1.0	1.0	1.0
Sales/Service Reps and Marketing Manager	4.0	4.0	4.0	4.0	4.0
Finance	1.0	1.0	1.0	1.0	1.0
Total	**16.0**	**24.0**	**31.0**	**39.0**	**45.0**

Most of the staff are support FTEs (phlebotomists, couriers, client services, sales, billers, and IT staff). Few technical FTEs are required, and only then in the more manual testing areas such as microbiology and cytology. The FTEs are added over time as the business grows.

The second problem with resources is a lack of timeliness in hiring them. Even profitable programs are subject to arcane approval processes and hiring freezes. When resources are eventually approved, the window of opportunity to bring on new business may be lost or the best resources may have gone to competitors. Why not allow the laboratory to hire staff as needed, as long as it is operating within budget and is accountable for business results?

Here is the moral of the story. If outreach is treated as a high organizational priority and as a separate business unit, it will thrive and generate material revenue and margin for the hospital. If it is handled as a low priority laboratory project, it will underperform. Organizations are perfectly designed to achieve their specific outcomes. If you want a different outcome, you have to choose a different design.

FINANCIAL RISK VERSUS BENEFITS

Everyone worries about the future. What will be the impact of known and unknown events on business strategy, profitability, perceived value, and priorities? And, let's be honest, personal risk is a factor. Is outreach the right or wrong decision, and how will my decision impact my personal reputation? Could it become a career-limiting decision? In health care, safety is valued more than risk.

Let's look at this question in a different way. This is not an absolute or final decision. In business, as in life, we often get caught up in looking too far into the future. What if laboratory becomes a commodity business? What if companies like Theranos make hospital laboratories irrelevant? What if point-of-care testing replaces centralized laboratories? What if wearable or implantable nanosensors monitor blood analytes on a real-time basis and report results to a smartphone?[1] I hear these questions all the time, but these are the *wrong* questions to be asking. They are too far into the future. What we really need to know is if outreach makes sense in the *near term*. I suggest we appraise outreach like a venture capitalist would look at any business decision:

- Will this business make money for the next five years?
- Do we understand the upside and downside risks and rewards?
- Do we have an exit strategy should conditions or priorities change?
- Are there other opportunities with better returns and lower risk?

If the answer to all of the above is yes, then focus on speed and execution. You are only going to have one chance at maximizing the impact for these next five years. You can change your mind along the way with minimal downside risk (as described in the Financial Considerations chapter). More importantly, you can maximize the returns in a reimbursement environment that is only very gradually declining. Remember that old expression "make hay while the sun shines?"

The problem is that health care is caught up in such gloom and doom that it is difficult to see opportunity, even if it may be time-limited of which no one is really sure. Remember the venture capitalist approach of the possibility of making money in the next five years. What if we are able to maintain margins during a gradual decline of reimbursement by continuous improvements in operational effectiveness? How else can we explain that reimbursement decline has been going on for decades and yet outreach program margins are currently at their highest? I know from personal experience with dozens of laboratories each year that there is always more untapped opportunity to reduce costs. If you are in doubt, watch my video on Chi's website called "What If My Lab Is Already Good?"

> ▶ We are in a classic inflection point. Because of the complexity and (incorrectly) perceived risk of outreach, I foresee fewer, larger, regional outreach programs in the future. However, this strategy is still viable today for hospitals with existing programs and for new startups.

We are at a classic inflection point. Because of the complexity and (incorrectly) perceived risk of outreach, I foresee fewer, larger, regional outreach programs in the future. However, this strategy is still viable today for hospitals with existing programs and for new startups. There may be a point in the future where returns diminish and the opportunity becomes less viable for the 20 percent of hospitals that do not have an outreach program today. We are not there yet. Of the 80 percent who are in the business today, those with a poorly run business will choose or be forced to exit. This is nothing different than what occurs in businesses all the time. Poorly run businesses are weeded out, and the well run survive.

THINK LIKE A VENTURE CAPITALIST #1:
DOES THE BUSINESS MAKE MONEY?

Let's examine the window of opportunity for new entrants. As shown in the table below, there is a range of $16 million to $20 million in new operating margin over five years for new startups. The return on investment (ROI) is an impressive 52 to 71 percent.

TABLE 10.4: RANGE OF FINANCIAL METRICS FOR NEW OUTREACH PROGRAMS

New Operating Margin	New Operating Margin (%)	Return on Investment
$16-20 million	28%-34%	52%-71%

What are the factors that have the largest influence on the range? The three biggest accelerators in order of importance are:

- The number of employed and affiliated physicians who do not currently use the hospital laboratory
- Spare capacity in staff and equipment
- An existing, competitive IT connectivity system

Working assumptions include a professional sales staff that generates $6,500 in new net revenue per month. Billing on the national laboratory fee schedule (to be competitive with Quest and LabCorp) is the second requirement for a new entrant. Lastly, we are assuming that all the components of a competitive infrastructure in place.

> ▶ The single largest accelerator is the market opportunity represented by employed primary care physicians. Many systems have a significant opportunity (several million dollars) that is not captured or has significant leakage.

The single largest accelerator is the market opportunity represented by employed primary care physicians. Many systems have a significant opportunity (several million dollars) that is not captured or has significant leakage. In the past year, we had a five-hospital system client in the Southwest, who employed about 100 primary care physicians and did not perform any of the laboratory work for this group. At $5,500 per month in new net revenue per physician, the cost of leakage to Quest and LabCorp was $6.6 million! Assuming a competitive offering, growth can be accelerated significantly in the first year of a new program with a concerted effort to win the business from employed physicians.

The second accelerator is a laboratory with spare capacity in equipment and staff. Virtually all laboratories have spare capacity on existing equipment to run additional volume on off-shifts. Rarely is new laboratory equipment required. Spare capacity in labor is not so easy to predict. Outreach is support staff-intensive, requiring the addition of phlebotomists, couriers, specimen processors, and client services staff. For technical staff, an additional one to two FTEs in total may be required for the more manual, labor-intensive areas such as microbiology and cytology and, perhaps, second shift in the automated laboratory. Any more than this is fluff. Outreach volume has to be processed and reported by the next morning. Unlike hospital work which must be turned around quickly, the laboratory has all of the second and third shifts to process the outreach volume and report results.

An existing IT connectivity system is the third accelerator. The Southwest hospital system referenced above had no physician office business, but it had a state-of-the-art connectivity system for a large reference laboratory client that could be dual-purposed. That saved the hospital a couple hundred thousand dollars in capital expense and the time (typically six to twelve months) to acquire and implement a connectivity system. In a five-year window, the gain or loss of one year has a material impact.

The ranges above are for new startups. What about those organizations that have existing programs? The expected profitability and rate of return for an ongoing business should be in the range of what is seen in years 4 and 5 of a startup, roughly 40 percent. You have already made the sunk costs. Now all you need is improved performance— a better mouse trap.

> ▶ Who isn't looking for this kind of new operating margin for their organization? I recently shared the more conservative side of the range ($10 million in operating margin over five years) with a CEO of a five-hospital system in the Southwest. He responded, "If outreach could bring in an additional $2 million to the bottom line every year, I'm in." What if that number were doubled? Would you be interested then?

Who isn't looking for this kind of new operating margin for their organization? I recently shared the more conservative side of the range ($10 million in operating margin over five years) with a CEO of a five-hospital system in the Southwest. He responded, "If outreach could bring in an additional $2 million to the bottom line every year, I'm in." What if that number were doubled? Would you be interested then? As you can see from above, this is doable with the right execution.

THINK LIKE A VENTURE CAPITALIST #2: DO WE UNDERSTAND THE RISKS AND REWARDS AND HAVE AN EXIT STRATEGY?

Now that we understand the opportunity for outreach, what are the risks and rewards? Let's do the reward first: $16 million to $20 million in new operating margin each year with a 52 to 71 percent ROI. Sure, that sounds good, but what are the downside risks? Naturally, we tend to focus more on the downside risks. What if the business environment changes to the point where outreach is no longer financially viable? What if your organizational priorities change? No problem. You have an exit strategy and, contrary to popular belief, it is fairly simple and straightforward to execute.

As discussed in detail in the Financial Considerations chapter, the business can be easily monetized. Current multiples are in the range of 1.0 to 1.5 times revenue. The multiple can be higher for specialty laboratories, but this number is typical of what we have seen in the industry over the last three to five years. And there are always willing buyers—both Quest and LabCorp have grown mostly by acquisition over the last few years.

Because the vast majority of investment for outreach is in operating expenses and, of that, most of the cost is labor, an exit strategy requires right-sizing staffing for reduced volume and eliminating outreach-specific FTEs (sales, couriers, phlebotomists, specimen processors, billing, and client services). No doubt, reductions in force are emotionally challenging but fairly straightforward from a business perspective.

▶ The risk associated with an outreach strategy is low. With a thoughtful analysis of options and good execution, it is easy to exit the business. The ability to monetize without timing constraints further supports a low-risk strategy.

In this context, the risk associated with an outreach strategy is low. With a thoughtful analysis of options and good execution, it is easy to exit the business. The ability to monetize without timing constraints further supports a low-risk strategy. Does that surprise you? I think it would surprise many executives who view outreach as difficult, complex, and risky.

THINK LIKE A VENTURE CAPITALIST #3: DO YOU HAVE A BETTER PLAN?

Health care organizations are so risk adverse that they tend to weigh the downside risk more than the upside benefits. That's all right, assuming you have alternate business plans. One of my favorite retorts to executives who talk solely about the negatives associated with outreach is to ask the following simple question, "*Do you have a better plan?*" Most often, said executive is speechless. This is the conundrum, the irrationality of health care. We know that focusing on cost reductions alone is not sufficient for long-term viability. What other plan do you have that will make more money with less risk? If nothing comes to mind, you owe it to your organization to evaluate outreach with a fresh, objective perspective. It is your fiduciary responsibility.

OTHER DOWNSTREAM BENEFITS

In addition to the expected benefits of new revenue and margin, there are five important, but less obvious, advantages to consider:

- Improved service (turnaround time) for all patient types
- Improved quality of results
- Unit cost lowered by 50 percent
- Improved population health management
- Increased productivity and utilization of spare capacity—why spend millions of dollars on equipment and only use 20 percent of capacity?

With expanded volume comes more frequent testing and improved turnaround time for all patient types. Getting into the outreach business indirectly helps the laboratory improve services to inpatients and outpatients by performing tests more frequently and reducing the turnaround time to results. Smaller volume tests that previously may have been referred to outside laboratories may be able to be insourced. The benefits of insourcing are two-fold: improved service and reduced cost.

Testing performed locally has the highest quality. The shorter the distance between the patient and the testing location, the less likely there will be specimen degradation and spurious results. Why would you want to risk spending specimens hundreds of miles under widely adverse conditions to a regional laboratory when you can perform the test locally?

There is also a substantial impact to unit costs. Outreach results in a lowering of cost per test by 50 percent.

Getting into the population health management game requires continuity of testing. Do you want to opt out of this by outsourcing a substantial portion of your testing to a commercial laboratory? Do you understand the risk of comparing results from different laboratories? Did you know that laboratory results are estimated to drive 60 to 70 percent of all decisions regarding a patient's diagnosis, treatment, hospital admission, and discharge?[2] Lastly, outreach improves productivity and makes appropriate use of inherent spare capacity. My guess is that the average hospital laboratory (without outreach) probably only uses 20 percent of its total capacity. Really? Can you justify the millions of dollars spent on all the sophisticated laboratory equipment and automation for a maximum inpatient/outpatient workload during only three hours of the 24-hour workday?

The downstream benefits taken together with the financial benefits make it hard to imagine how any hospital can justify not doing outreach today.

BACK TO THE BEGINNING

So, if outreach provides so much benefit at relatively low risk at a time when hospitals and systems are starved for new money and desirous of improving services and lowering costs, why is there such confusion about the value of outreach? For that answer, we have to go back to *Chapter 2: Why Is Outreach So Misunderstood* and the concept of outreach as a self-fulfilling prophecy. If we believe that outreach is too hard, too complicated, a commodity business, non-core, etc., then that's what it will be. What we believe becomes a self-fulfilling prophecy (see Figure 10.2).

Because hospitals are not intentionally designed for outreach, it takes considerable knowledge, effort, and tenacity to succeed. Of these, the most important is tenacity. At times, it will seem that there are endless obstacles to overcome. Leadership experts say that, out of every ten executives who really want to achieve something great, three or four will make some progress and no more than one out of ten will actually achieve great things.[3] The following quote from Lee Thayer is a bitter pill to swallow:

> *"Most people prefer a problem they cannot solve to a solution they don't like."* [4]

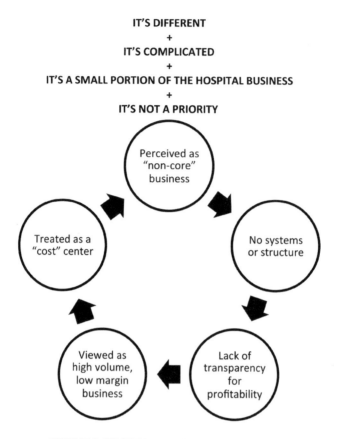

FIGURE 10.2: THE SELF-FULFILLING PROPHECY OF OUTREACH

This is especially true in the highly disruptive environment of health care today. With a focus on day-to-day survival, "most executives will go on being pretty much like they are." If the challenge is how to create a great outreach organization among all the other organizational priorities, nothing really changes day-to-day or year-to-year. The reason, Thayer explains, is that the effort and political capital required is more than they are willing to expend, so instead they "deal with the problems of mediocrity—and all of the insoluble problems that go with the nurturing of, or tolerance for, mediocrity,"[5] and never quite get around to achieving greatness.

You have a chance to be great. You have the road map.

What are you waiting for?

CHAPTER SUMMARY

A fresh view of the risks and rewards of outreach shows that outreach is a powerful triple play:

· Decreases unit costs by up to 50 percent and generates new operating margin of $16 million to $20 million in the first five years and building thereafter.

· Improves service for all patient types: outreach, outpatient, and inpatient alike.

· Provides for better quality through continuity of testing across the health continuum and enables better utilization and outcome managementIt's time to look at outreach anew or, perhaps, again and ask yourself why you haven't maximized this opportunity. Most likely the business was misunderstood, mismanaged, or misaligned. Perhaps you were misled by third parties with much to gain? None of that matters, because that is all in the past.

What is important now is that you know how to leverage your laboratory to make it a profit machine. Once you know something, you cannot "unknow" it. You have no alternative but to take action.

ACKNOWLEDGEMENTS

I want to thank my mentor, Alan Weiss, who convinced me that I could write this book and guided me through the process. Were it not for him, I would never have believed that I could do it and I would have neither tried nor succeeded in this effort.

Next, I thank my faithful assistant, Shannon Donahue, who did all the initial formatting, editing, and proofing, and also provided oversight and project management to keep me on track and on time. And to my editor, Linda Popky, who guided me through the publication process and provided valuable insights on content.

To the rest of the Chi team that supported me with ideas, critique and content—Jeff Myers, Jim Root, Julie Stein, Susan Dougherty, Dori Cheng, and Karla Yurgaites—thank you for all your support.

Finally, to my family, especially my sister, Ellen, who put up with my year-long distraction and provided much needed support so that I could have time to write.

I am lucky to have all these people in my life.

NOTES

Chapter 1

1. "Hospital and Laboratory Firm Join Forces in Commercial Lab," *Modern Healthcare*, June 1984.

2. "Regulatory Uncertainty Amid Flourishing Business Ventures Between Hospitals and Physicians," *National Intelligence Report*, February 14, 1984, 3-4.

Chapter 2

1. Chi Solutions, *Thirteenth Comprehensive National Laboratory Outreach Survey*, June 2014.

2. Beth Kutscher, "Fewer Hospitals Have Positive Margins as They Face Financial Squeeze," *Modern Healthcare*, June 21, 2014, http://www.modernhealthcare .com/article/20140621/MAGAZINE/306219968.

3. Chi Solutions, *Eleventh Comprehensive National Laboratory Outreach Survey*, June 2012.

Chapter 3

1. Robert S. Kaplan and David P. Norton, "The Balanced Scorecard: Measures That Drive Performance," *Harvard Business Review*, January–February 1992, 71-79.

2. American College of Healthcare Executives, "Top Issues Confronting Hospitals: 2014," *Healthcare Executive* 30, no. 2 (March/April 2015): 90.

3. Beth Kutscher, "Fewer Hospitals Have Positive Margins as They Face Financial Squeeze," *Modern Healthcare*, June 21, 2014, http://www.modernhealthcare .com/article/20140621/MAGAZINE/306219968.

4. William Edmondson, "The Per Capita Payment Model," *Journal of Healthcare Management* 60, no. 1 (January/February 2015): 16.

Chapter 4

1. L. Eleanor J. Herriman, Jenny Xu, and Jennifer Musimeci, *U.S. Clinical Laboratory and Pathology Testing 2013-2015: Market Analysis, Trends, and Forecasts* (Keene, NH: Kennedy Information/G2 Intelligence, 2013), 11.

2. Jeffrey H. Myers, "Revenue Risk and Price Transparency in Hospital-Based Laboratories," *Healthcare Financial Management*, November 2015, https://www .hfma.org/Content.aspx?id=42934.

3. "Proposed Rule Excludes Data from Most Hospital Labs to Reprice Lab Tests," *Laboratory Economics*, October 2015, 4.

4. Chi Solutions, *Fourteenth Comprehensive National Laboratory Outreach Survey*, August 2015.

5. Quest Diagnostics, Form 10-K (SEC filing), February 24, 2015, 2, http://ir.questdiagnostics.com/phoenix.zhtml?c=82068&p=irol-sec&secCat01.1_rs=71&secCat01.1_rc=10.

6. Ibid.

7. John Carreyrou, "Hot Startup Theranos Has Struggled With Its Blood Test Technology," *Wall Street Journal*, October 15, 2015, http://www.wsj.com/articles/theranos-has-struggled-with-blood-tests-1444881901; and John Carreyrou, "Hot Startup Theranos Dials Back Lab Tests at FDA's Behest," *Wall Street Journal*, October 16, 2015, http://www.wsj.com/articles/hot-startup-theranos-dials-back-lab-tests-at-fdas-behest-1444961864.

8. Andrew Pollack and Reed Abelson, "Theranos, a Blood Test Start-Up, Faces F.D.A. Scrutiny," *New York Times*, October 16, 2015, http://www.nytimes.com/2015/10/17/business/theranos-a-blood-test-start-up-faces-fda-scrutiny.html; Andrew Pollack, "Theranos, Facing Criticism, Says It Has Changed Board Structure," *New York Times*, October 28, 2015, http://www.nytimes.com/2015/10/29/business/theranos-facing-criticism-says-it-has-changed-board-structure.html; and James B. Stewart, "The Narrative Frays for Theranos and Elizabeth Holmes," *New York Times*, October 29, 2015, http://www.nytimes.com/2015/10/30/business/the-narrative-frays-for-theranos-and-elizabeth-holmes.html.

9. Christopher Weaver, Michael Siconolfi, and John Carreyrou, "Walgreens Threatens to End Theranos Agreement," *Wall Street Journal*, February 10, 2016, http://www.wsj.com/articles/walgreens-threatens-to-end-theranos-agreement-1455156503.

Chapter 5

1. Michael E. Porter, "What is Strategy?" *Harvard Business Review*, November-December 1996, 61-78.

2. Ibid., 61-69.

3. Ibid., 75.

Chapter 6

1. Chi Solutions, *Thirteenth Comprehensive National Laboratory Outreach Survey*, June 2014.

Chapter 7

1. Melinda Beck, "How to Bring the Price of Health Care into the Open," *Wall Street Journal*, February 23, 2014, http://www.wsj.com/articles/SB1000142405 2702303650204579375242842086688.

2. Ibid.

3. Derived from "Quest Diagnostics 2013: Profits Up, Revenue Down," *Laboratory Economics*, February 2014, 8.

4. Derived from "LabCorp 2013: Profits Down 1.6%; Revenue Up 2.4% on Acquisitions," *Laboratory Economics*, February 2014, 7.

Chapter 8

1. Stephen R. Covey, *The 7 Habits of Highly Effective People: Powerful Lessons in Personal Change* (New York: Simon and Schuster, 2004), 102.

Chapter 9

1. James M. Root, "Laboratory Sales and Service Representative Compensation: 2011 Survey Results and Analysis" (presentation, 4th Annual LabCompete: Laboratory Sales and Marketing Conference, Chandler, AZ, December 12-14, 2011).

2. Ibid.

3. Ibid.

Chapter 10

1. Eric J. Topol, *The Patient Will See You Now: The Future of Medicine Is in Your Hands* (New York: Basic Books, 2015).

2. Rodney W. Forsman, "Why is the Laboratory an Afterthought for Managed Care Organizations?" *Clinical Chemistry* 42, no. 5 (1996): 813.

3. Lee Thayer, *Leadership: Thinking, Being, Doing* (Rochester, NY: WME Books, 2007).

4. Ibid., 15.

5. Ibid., 15-16.

REFERENCES

American College of Healthcare Executives. "Top Issues Confronting Hospitals: 2014." *Healthcare Executive* 30, no. 2 (March/April 2015): 90.

Beck, Melinda. "How to Bring the Price of Health Care into the Open." *Wall Street Journal*, February 23, 2014. http://www.wsj.com/articles/SB10001424052702303650204579375242842086688.

Carreyrou, John. "Hot Startup Theranos Dials Back Lab Tests at FDA's Behest." *Wall Street Journal*, October 16, 2015. http://www.wsj.com/articles/hot-startup-theranos-dials-back-lab-tests-at-fdas-behest-1444961864.

Carreyrou, John. "Hot Startup Theranos Has Struggled With Its Blood Test Technology." *Wall Street Journal*, October 15, 2015. http://www.wsj.com/articles/theranos-has-struggled-with-blood-tests-1444881901.

Chi Solutions, *Fourteenth Comprehensive National Laboratory Outreach Survey*, August 2015.

Chi Solutions, *Thirteenth Comprehensive National Laboratory Outreach Survey*, June 2014.

Chi Solutions, *Eleventh Comprehensive National Laboratory Outreach Survey*, June 2012.

Covey, Stephen R. *The 7 Habits of Highly Effective People: Powerful Lessons in Personal Change.* New York: Simon and Schuster, 2004.

Edmondson, William. "The Per Capita Payment Model." *Journal of Healthcare Management* 60, no. 1 (January/February 2015): 14–16.

Forsman, Rodney W. "Why is the Laboratory an Afterthought for Managed Care Organizations?" *Clinical Chemistry* 42, no. 5 (1996): 813–816.

Herriman, L. Eleanor J., Jenny Xu, and Jennifer Musimeci. *U.S. Clinical Laboratory and Pathology Testing 2013-2015: Market Analysis, Trends, and Forecasts.* Keene, NH: Kennedy Information/G2 Intelligence, 2013.

Kaplan, Robert S., and David P. Norton. "The Balanced Scorecard: Measures That Drive Performance." *Harvard Business Review*, January-February 1992.

Kutscher, Beth. "Fewer Hospitals Have Positive Margins as They Face Financial Squeeze." *Modern Healthcare*, June 21, 2014. http://www.modernhealthcare.com/article/20140621/MAGAZINE/306219968.

Laboratory Economics. "LabCorp 2013: Profits Down 1.6%; Revenue Up 2.4% on Acquisitions." February 2014.

Laboratory Economics. "Quest Diagnostics 2013: Profits Up, Revenue Down." February 2014.

Laboratory Economics. "Proposed Rule Excludes Data from Most Hospital Labs to Reprice Lab Tests." October 2015.

Modern Healthcare. "Hospital and Laboratory Firm Join Forces in Commercial Lab." June 1984.

Myers, Jeffrey H. "Revenue Risk and Price Transparency in Hospital-Based Laboratories." *Healthcare Financial Management*, November 2015. https://www.hfma.org/Content.aspx?id=42934.

National Intelligence Report. "Regulatory Uncertainty Amid Flourishing Business Ventures Between Hospitals and Physicians." February 14, 1984.

Pollack, Andrew. "Theranos, Facing Criticism, Says It Has Changed Board Structure." *New York Times*, October 28, 2015. http://www.nytimes.com/2015/10/29/business/theranos-facing-criticism-says-it-has-changed-board-structure.html.

Pollack, Andrew, and Reed Abelson. "Theranos, a Blood Test Start-Up, Faces F.D.A. Scrutiny." *New York Times*, October 16, 2015. http://www.nytimes.com/2015/10/17/business/theranos-a-blood-test-start-up-faces-fda-scrutiny.html.

Porter, Michael E. "What is Strategy?" *Harvard Business Review*, November-December 1996.

Quest Diagnostics. *Form 10-K*. SEC filing, February 24, 2015. http://ir.questdiagnostics.com/phoenix.zhtml?c=82068&p=irol-sec&secCat01.1_rs=71&secCat01.1_rc=10.

Root, James M. "Laboratory Sales and Service Representative Compensation: 2011 Survey Results and Analysis." Presentation at the 4th Annual LabCompete: Laboratory Sales and Marketing Conference, Chandler, AZ, December 12-14, 2011.

Stewart, James B. "The Narrative Frays for Theranos and Elizabeth Holmes." *New York Times*, October 29, 2015. http://www.nytimes.com/2015/10/30/business/the-narrative-frays-for-theranos-and-elizabeth-holmes.html.

Thayer, Lee. *Leadership: Thinking, Being, Doing*. Rochester, NY: WME Books, 2007.

Topol, Eric J. *The Patient Will See You Now: The Future of Medicine Is in Your Hands*. New York: Basic Books, 2015.

Weaver, Christopher, Michael Siconolfi, and John Carreyrou. "Walgreens Threatens to End Theranos Agreement." *Wall Street Journal*, February 10, 2016. http://www.wsj.com/articles/walgreens-threatens-to-end-theranos-agreement-1455156503.

INDEX

80/20 rule 61

A

Accountable care organizations (ACO) 30
Accounting 15-17, 99, 104
ACD (automated call distribution) 74
ACLA (American Clinical Laboratory
    Association) 3
ACO (accountable care organizations) 30
Acquisition 5, 93
Accumen 102
Affordable Care Act 39, 53, 81-82
Aging 39, 53
Allegheny Health 48
American Clinical Laboratory Association
    (ACLA) 3
Anti-markup laws 3
Aptitude tests 110
Automated call distribution (ACD) 74-75
Automation 30, 74-75

B

Bad debt rate 21, 86
Balanced scorecard (BSC) 23, 30
Benchmarking 73-74, 92, 124-125
Billing 14, 40, 66, 74-75, 78, 86
    duplicate 5
    efficiency of 66, 86, 91
    outsourcing of 86-87, 95
Bioran 3
Bio-Reference Laboratories 35
Biskind Laboratory 2
Blood collection 50, 61, 66, 70-71, 75,
    88, 127
Bristol-Meyers 3
Brown, Paul 2
BSC (balanced scorecard) 23
Budget 40, 97
Business models 18, 27, 48-50, 53,
    61-64, 102
Business plan 97, 133-134

C

Caliper 110
Call centers 74
Capacity iii, 26, 30, 32, 65, 71, 75, 131, 134
Capitation 5-6
Care, accountable iii
    continuum of 30-32 77-78, 101, 137
    long-term 31
    managed iii, 5-6, 79-80, 95
Centers for Medicare and Medicaid
    Services (CMS) 32, 43-44, 51
Cerner 67
Chain of services 14
Chi Solutions 15, 19-22, 25, 36, 47, 66, 81,
    86, 89, 92, 100, 102, 104, 118, 121,
    127, 130
Claim denials 91
Cleveland Clinic 51
CLIA (Clinical Laboratory Improvement
    Act) 2
Client services 21, 74
Clinical Laboratory Improvement Act
    (CLIA) 2
CMS (Centers for Medicare and Medicaid
    Services) 32, 43-44, 51
Collections 86, 91
Communications 107
Competitive advantage 55-60, 74
Competitive convergence 59
*Comprehensive National Laboratory Outreach
    Survey* 15, 20-22, 25, 45, 81, 85-86,
    100, 107, 113, 117, 124
Consulting 15-16, 19-20, 36, 72, 89,
    114, 123
Continental Airlines 59
Contract research organization (CRO) 7
Contracting, managed care 79-80, 95
Contracts, exclusive 6
Co-pays 81
Corning Clinical Laboratories 5
Corporate integrity 5-6, 8

Cost, allocation of 15-17, 26, 29-30, 42-43
    management of 25
    market-based 43
    misallocation of 15, 88
    reduction of iii, 5, 32, 40-41, 49, 87, 92
    variable 26, 28
Cost curve 23
Couriers 21, 27, 61, 69, 71, 74, 88, 93, 127
Covance 7
CRM (customer relationship management)
    120-121
CRO (contract research organization) 7
Customer relationship management
    (CRM) 120-121
Cytology 72, 88

D

Damon Clinical Laboratories 3
Data submission, uneven 43-44
Days sales outstanding (DSO) 21, 86
Deductibles 81
Diagnosis and treatment 63, 134
Diagnosis-related groups (DRGs) iii, 5
Diagnostics 114
Dignity Health 51
Direct billing laws 3
Divergence 58, 64
DRGs (diagnosis related groups) iii, 5
Drug development 7
DSO (days sales outstanding) 21, 86

E

EBITDA (earnings before interest, taxes,
    depreciation, and amortization)
    24, 65, 77, 95, 127
Edmondson, William 30
Eighty-Twenty Rule 61
Electronic medical record (EMR) 40, 52,
    67, 69, 127
EMR (electronic medical record) 40, 52,
    67, 69, 127
Epic 67
EXCEL 120
Exit strategy 93-95, 129, 133

F

Facilities, low-profitability 29, 35-36
FDA (Food and Drug Administration) 51

Financial transparency 78, 81, 88, 124
FTEs (full time equivalents) 66, 72, 88,
    93-94, 127-128, 131, 133
Full time equivalents (FTEs) 66, 72, 88,
    93-94, 127-128, 131, 133

G

GlaxoSmithKline 51
Government investigation 5, 51
Government payers 30, 43
Growth, through acquisition 6-7, 26, 93

H

Hallmark 48
Harvard Business Review 55
Harvard Business School 23
Health care companies, non-laboratory 7
Health care costs, industry adaptation 31
Health care industry, disruption of iii, 7, 48,
    51, 53, 64, 136
Health care, provider and payer relationship
    48
Health systems, accountability of 30
    efficiency of 30-31
    outcome-orientation of 30
Healthcare Executive 25
Holmes, Elizabeth 50-51
Hospital CEOs, poll of 24-25
Hospital laboratories 4, 6-7, 29-31, 53,
    89, 123
    captive business practices of 4, 12-14
    competitiveness of 44-45, 53
    consolidation of 6, 27, 44, 92, 100
    costs of iii, 27-28, 32
    incentives to exclude 80, 88
    poor service of 11-14
    revenue sharing 31, 35
    See also Laboratories
Hospital outreach iii, 4, 6-7, 123
    as entrepreneurial business 15, 71
    non-business management of 15,
        19-21, 88, 98, 104
    operating margin of 16-17, 20, 25-26,
        32, 66, 95, 130, 132, 137
    profitability of 17, 20-21, 26, 66,
        95, 132
Hunt Big Sales 36, 117

I

ICN Pharmaceuticals 3
Imaging 114
Imitation 56, 59-60
Implementation 63, 123
Information technology (IT) 17, 40, 62-63,
    65, 67, 69, 72, 74-75, 89, 93, 97,
    131-132
Infrastructure 29, 65, 67, 69, 73, 131
Initial public offering (IPO) 103-104
Inreach 37, 66, 85
Insourcing 134
Insurance companies 6-7, 30, 79-80-81,
    126
Insurance premiums 82
Insurance, commercial 6-7, 30, 126
Intermountain Healthcare 51
IPO (initial public offering) 103-104
IT (information technology) 17, 40,
    62-63, 65, 67, 69, 72, 74-75,
    89, 93, 97, 131-132

J

Jenny Edmunson Hospital 4
Joint Venture Hospital Laboratories
    (JVHL) 6
Joint ventures 45, 101, 103-104

K

Kaplan and Norton 23
Key performance indicators (KPI) 21, 104
Kings County Research Laboratory 1
KPI (key performance indicators) 21, 104

L

LabCorp iii, 6-9, 25-26, 35, 42-44, 46-48,
    53, 68, 70, 80, 82, 87, 93, 101-102,
    107-108, 131, 133
Laboratories, chain of services 13
    independent 1-7, 43, 45, 85, 87, 100
    licensing of 2
    offsite 5, 100
    physician partnership 4
    redundancy of 31-32
    strategic options 56
    See also Hospital laboratories
Laboratory Corporation of America 6;
    see LabCorp

Laboratory Economics 43
Laboratory practices, physician perception
    of 37-39
Laboratory Procedures (company) 2
Laboratory, 'smart' 62-63
Laboratory 114
    as economic engine iv, 65, 75, 77
    autonomy of iv
    continuum of care 29
    high service 61
    infrastructure redundancy 29
    low cost 60-61
    mega 6
    no frills service 60-61
    profit potential of iv, 65
    smart 62-63
    trends 40-41, 52, 100, 129
Labscam 5
Leverage, negotiating 6, 48, 80-81

M

M&A (merger and acquisition) 6
MacNeal Memorial Hospital 5
Makeover, business 55
Management, intuitive 104
Management reports 21, 97, 104
Margin, contribution 87, 100
    operating iv, 16, 25-26, 32, 66, 87,
        95, 132
    profitability 15, 20, 24-25, 87, 95
Market opportunity 37-39
Market segments 32-38, 53
Marketing 107
Mayo Clinic 4
Medical assistants 61
Medical home 31
Medical Laboratory Network 4
Medical technologists 61, 74
Medicare 5, 43
Merger and acquisition (M&A) 6
Meris Lab 4
MetPath 2-5
Metrics for client service 21
Microbiology 72, 88
Modern Healthcare 4
Mom-and-pop iv, 65, 76, 88, 121

N

National Health Laboratories 6
National Intelligence Report 5
New York Times 50
Nichols Management Group 102
Nonpatients 13, 124, 126
Nonprofit hospitals 93, 98
  business challenges 19, 98
  decision making 19
Nursing facilities 29

O

Online order entry systems 91
Operating margin iv, 16, 26, 32, 66,
  95, 130, 137
Operational strategies 56
Outpatient iv, 12, 23, 29-30, 42, 81
Outreach iii, 4-6, 25, 35, 45, 65, 74, 77,
  98, 130
  capital requirements of 67, 93, 126-127
  competitive disadvantages of 40, 127
  constraints of 123
  financial rationale for 25, 29
  infrastructure of 13-14, 131
  models 45
  multiple hospital program 23, 45,
    68, 114, 132
  negative perceptions of iv, 11-15,
    22, 123
  performance versus independent
    laboratories 4, 12-13, 16, 25-26,
    28-29, 32, 45-47, 53, 73
  profitability of 15, 20, 24-26, 45-46,
    83, 87, 92, 95, 132
  single hospital program 45
Overhead 15

P

P&L (profit and loss) iii, 15, 17, 21, 75,
  88-89, 97, 104, 124
PAMA (Protecting Access to Medicare Act
  of 2014) 32, 43-44
PAML (Pathology Associates Medical
  Laboratories) 101
Partnering 48-49, 53
Partnerships, non-equity 102-103
Pathologists 1-2, 4-5, 40, 61
Pathology Associates Medical Laboratories
  (PAML) 101

Patient 31
  accountability 31
  care teams 62-63
  dissatisfied 12
  outcomes 63
Patient service center (PSC) 11-13, 66,
  69-70, 75, 93, 127
Pfizer 51
Pharmaceutical companies 1-6
Phlebotomy 61, 66, 70-71, 75, 88, 127
Physician partnership laboratories 4-5
Physicians 67
  affiliated 37, 131
  intervention of 63, 134
  laboratory ordering practices of 37-38,
    67
  offices of 33, 35, 70, 84
  primary care 37, 63, 131
  referrals by 37
  specialists 37, 63
POLs (physician office laboratories) 31,
  43-44, 53
Population health management iv, 30,
  78, 134
Porter, Michael 55-60, 64
Pricing 4, 19-20, 40, 43-44, 78, 81, 83,
  95, 124
Private equity companies 7
Profit and loss (P&L) iii, 15, 17, 21, 75, 88,
  97, 104, 123
Profit margin 15, 20, 24-25, 87, 95
Profitability 17, 20-21, 26, 83, 92, 95,
  119, 132
Profit-sharing 101-102
Protecting Access to Medicare Act of 2014
  (PAMA) 32, 43-44
PSC (patient service center) 11-13, 66,
  69-70, 75, 93, 127

Q

Quality 134
Quest Diagnostics iii, 6-9, 25-26, 35, 42-44,
  46-48, 53, 68, 70, 80, 82, 87, 93,
  101-102, 107-108, 131, 133
Quest Diagnostics, CEO of 48-49

R

Rate cuts 43
Recurring revenue model 23, 107, 122
Reduction in force 94

Regionalization 5-6, 29, 46
Registration process 12
Regulation 4
Regulatory compliance 116
Rehabilitation facilities 29
Reimbursement 78, 87, 129
    declining 5, 23-24, 42, 45, 53, 87
    fixed 5
    higher for hospital laboratories 26,
        32, 40, 42-44, 81, 85
    Medicare 5
    performance-based 19
    standardized 26, 32, 85
Reports, management 21, 97
Research, role of laboratory testing in 39
Revenue iii, 4, 15, 20, 23-25, 33, 40, 42,
        92, 113
    compounding of 108
    per requisition 25-26
    projection of 119
    segregation of 66, 99
Revlon 3
Risk aversion 25, 85, 93, 129, 133
Risk mitigation 25, 129
Roche Biomedical Laboratories 6
Root Associates 4
Rule of 78 108
Rusckowski, Stephen 48-49

S

Safeway 51
Sales 40, 75, 107
    management of 112-115, 118, 122
    performance 91, 117-118, 122
    plan 117-118
Sales representatives 107-110
    compensation models for 111-112
    laboratory specialists as 107, 113-114
    non-performing 115
    screening of 110-112
    training of 116-117
Scale, economy of 23, 27-29, 32, 78-79
Searcy, Tom 36, 117
SmithKline Beecham 2
Software, physician connectivity 127, 132
Sonic 101
Southwest Airlines 56-59
Spare capacity iii, 26, 30, 32, 65, 71, 75,
        131, 134

Specimens, collection sites for 12, 69
    transportation of 61, 69, 71, 127
St. Joseph Hospital 4
Standardization 43-44, 61, 92
Stark anti-kickback statutes 116
Straddling 59, 64
Strategic positioning 56-60
Structure, operational 97-100, 102-105,
        123-125
Sunk costs iii

T

Tax Equity and Fiscal Responsibility Act
        of 1982 (TEFRA) 5
Taxation 101
TEFRA (Tax Equity and Fiscal
        Responsibility Act of 1982) 5
Tests, affordability of 39
    development of 39, 53
    underutilization of 39
Testing 32, 49-50, 53, 62, 74
    algorithms of 63
    anatomic pathology 32, 53
    direct access to 49-50
    drug 32
    duplication of 29-30, 62
    fixed fee 1
    fragmentation of 29
    immunology 32
    inpatient 81
    irregularities 29, 50, 74, 135
    local 134
    molecular and esoteric 32, 35, 53
    origin of 35, 53
    point of care 49-50
    reflex 5-6
    routine 32, 35, 53
    sequencing of 31
    unnecessary 5
Thayer, Lee 135-136
Theranos 50-51, 129
    CEO of 50-51
    proprietary methodology of 50-51
    relationship with Walgreens 50-51
Training, compliance 115
Turnaround-time-to-results 26-27, 40, 42,
        73-75, 91, 134

U

UBI (unrelated business income) 100-101
UML (United Medical Laboratories) 1, 3
Unit cost iv, 23, 28, 32, 78, 83-84, 91,
        134, 137
United Healthcare 46
United Medical Laboratories (UML) 1, 3
United West Labs 102
Unrelated business income (UBI) 100-101
Upjohn 2

V

Venture capitalist, thought process of
        129-130
Visiting nurses 61
Volume
    growth of 5, 65, 134
    impact of 27-28, 30, 53, 71, 78, 92, 95

W

W. R. Grace 3
Wait times 12
Walgreens 50-51
Wall Street Journal 50-51, 82
What is Strategy? Article 55
Write-off balance 92

ABOUT THE AUTHOR

Kathleen A. Murphy, PhD, is a laboratory scientist turned executive and entrepreneur. *The Profit Machine in the Hospital Basement: Turning Your Lab into an Economic Engine* is her first book.

Kathy is the chief executive officer of Chi Solutions, Inc., a clinical laboratory management and consulting firm headquartered in Ann Arbor, Michigan. Chi Solutions is founded on the principle that hospitals can compete with large national and regional laboratories through consolidation, regionalization, and outreach. Every laboratory has spare capacity that it can leverage to secure additional test volume from the community. With a competitive offering in place, laboratory outreach programs that are operated and financed as serious business entities can match or outpace Quest Diagnostics, LabCorp, and similar competitors.

An early adopter of the laboratory outreach strategy, Kathy started two successful programs in Boston in the 1980s and 1990s. By sharing more than three decades of knowledge about running a profitable outreach business, she has devoted her career to teaching hospitals how to commercialize their laboratories to capture new revenue and counteract declining reimbursements.

Kathy's personal interests include gardening, photography, travel, and volunteer work. She serves on the Board of Trustees and the Foundation Board for her undergraduate alma mater, Salem State University in Salem, Massachusetts.